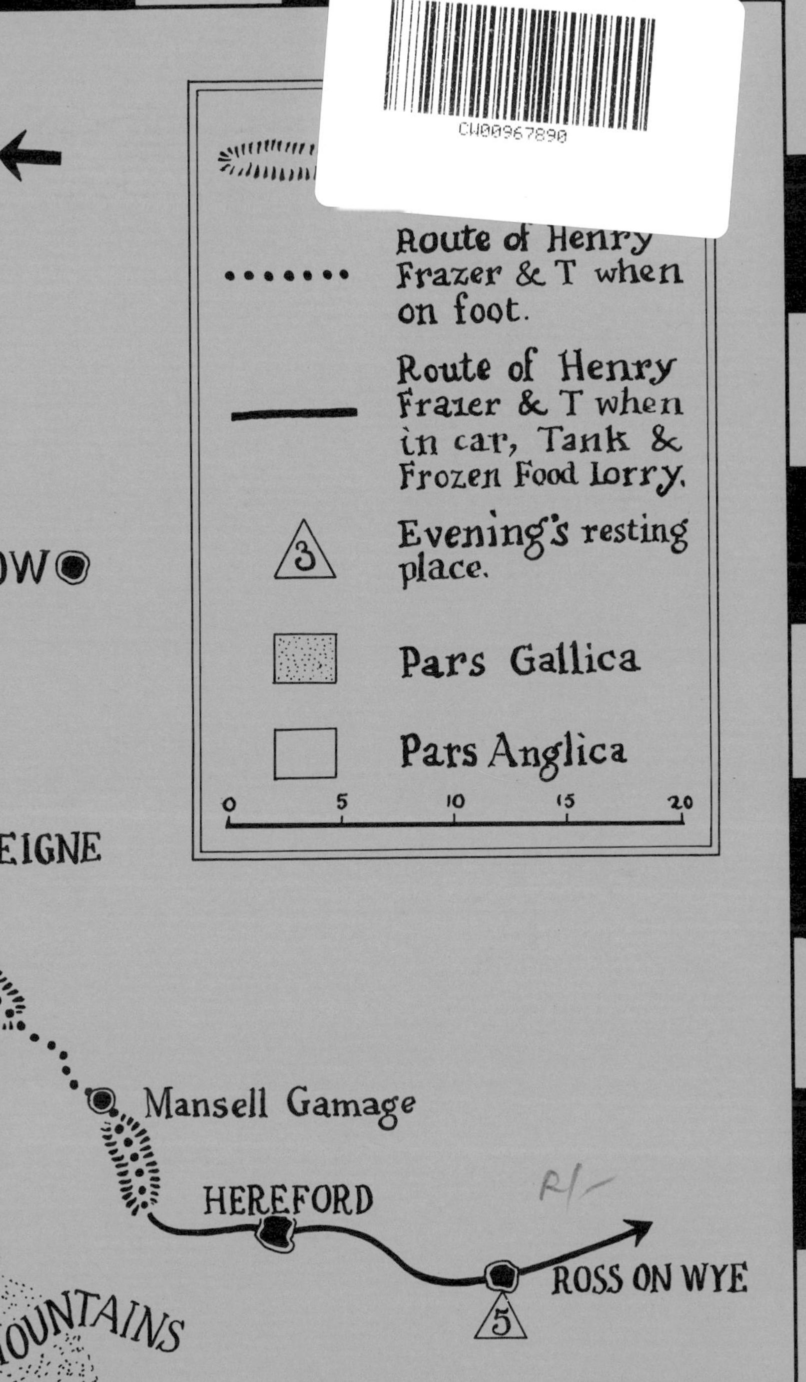

Route of Henry
Frazer & T when
on foot.
Route of Henry
Frazer & T when
in car, Tank &
Frozen Food lorry.
Evening's resting
place.
Pars Gallica
Pars Anglica
0
5
10
15
20
OW
EIGNE
Mansell Gamage
HEREFORD
ROSS ON WYE
MOUNTAINS

THREE MEN (NOT) IN A BOAT

# THREE MEN (NOT) IN A BOAT

*and most of the time without a dog*

TIMOTHY FINN

with drawings by Shoo Rayner

Duckworth

First published in 1983 by
Gerald Duckworth & Co. Ltd.
The Old Piano Factory
43 Gloucester Crescent, London, NW1



ISBN 0 7156 1717 6

Photoset in North Wales by
Derek Doyle & Associates, Mold, Clwyd
Printed in Great Britain by
Ebenezer Baylis & Son Limited
The Trinity Press, Worcester and London

# Contents

To Peter Lund

# 1

# Talking it Over

Fraser said: 'What about the Lyke Wake Walk in November?'

Henry and I looked at each other knowingly.

It's a thing you have to watch with Fraser, this question of dates. Most ordinary mortals, as you know – the you's and me's of this world – carry around through life a handy little booklet known as a diary, into which they write whatever they may be doing in the future. Then, as each day comes along, they can put their nose round the corner of the page to see if they are supposed to be up to anything or whether they can go back to bed again. And if it's an expensive type of diary they can get all sorts of extra information on how to convert hectares into roods and whether it is a public holiday in Jakarta. That is how people's timetables are planned.

Not Fraser's.

Fraser is one of that other band of people who run their timetable on what is called the Navigational Principle. The Navigational Principle involves no paperwork at all. The single technique is to seize on any appointment which falls within one's mental horizon and keep it to the minute, while other more distant events are given a wide berth, lost in the fog, thrown overboard, or allocated to a time so remote that nobody can seriously expect you to stick to them anyway.

*That* was why Fraser suggested 'November'.

That was why Henry and I looked at each other knowingly.

We were talking about a holiday. Fraser said he was exhausted and needed a break. Not only that, but his future programme was so full that if we couldn't grab the opportunity within the next few days we would have to count him out till 'November'.

Henry said he was exhausted too, but since he was treading the boards in the local production of *Blithe Spirit* the week after next, any idea of slipping off was quite out of the question for the next fortnight or so. (All this, of course, was nothing more than theatrical bluff on Henry's part. Henry wasn't treading the boards and never will. What Henry was doing was Stage Managing, which – as he interprets the rôle – involves nothing more than hanging around the dressing rooms telling all the performers that it's nothing like as funny as the Russian tragedy they did last year.)

I also was exhausted. But I rose above this quibbling over departure times: 'At least,' I said, 'we're all agreed on one thing. A holiday is sorely needed.'

I must say, one isn't looking for applause and back-slapping from one's friends when one makes a simple man-to-man remark like the one I had just uttered. An approving nod, a fish-like waggle of the wrist is quite enough to show that old companions are on the same wavelength. What one has no right to expect is a sarcastic clearing of the throat and an 'Oh ... ah ... um' from Fraser, and one of those maddening, mindless cackles of a laugh from Henry as if to say 'Go on – pull the other one'.

I knew what they were on about of course, and it's a lie which I shall nail to the floor if I have to live to be a hundred to do it. *They* were the busy ones – that was what they were thinking. *I* was the slacker. *They* did their eight hours grind a day. *I* dawdled my time away in listless sybaritism and ease.

It is one of the crosses you have to bear when you become an author that nobody believes you do any *work* at all.

'Sorry we can't help you change your tyre,' Henry and Fraser will say as Mrs Wilby from the post-office runs over the same rusty nail for the third time in a week. 'We're off to work. Try T,' they say. 'Old T will give you a hand.'

'But isn't he busy as well?'

'Who – T? Busy?' they will murmur with smiles. 'Oh, no. T's not busy. He has nothing to do. Just lolls around all day with his feet up. Between you and us he'd jump at the chance of having something to keep him occupied.'

I'd jump all right. Jump with anger. Fraser and Henry may find it amusing to describe my working stance as 'lolling around', but they know perfectly well how unfair that is. What I am doing, of course, is adopting an attitude of maximum concentration, poised to snatch at any idea which may happen to float by me in the course of the day. The posture is critical: feet up, so as to increase the flow of blood to the brain where it is most likely to be needed, eyes closed to sharpen the senses, hands behind the head so that I know where to find them if I have to write anything down suddenly.

I have known authors who can stretch out, apparently unconscious, in front of a radio set and then wake up and remember whole monologues from Edward Heath on the need for interface with the Third World. I've even heard of one who can say the monologues backwards and make them seem just as meaningful as they did the right way round. That's concentration for you – and you don't need me to tell you that you can't reach that pitch of perfection without a lifetime of training and self-discipline. It's all too easy for a young writer nowadays to abandon himself to frivolous pleasures and simply fritter his time away in changing car tyres, taking the children to school, rodding out drains, doing the washing up, and generally listening to the thousand-and-one siren voices which would lure him away from a life of dedication and hard work – I've done it myself in my time. Now I know better, and any indulgence of that sort is strictly kept back for the proper place and time – Easter Bank Holiday Monday in my book.

I had an object lesson in concentration at quite a young age. It was just after I had left university, when I did two or three months in an advertising agency as Personal Assistant to the Chairman, Sir Hector Botulus. Sir Hector was an important man in his profession, and he had risen to such a position of eminence that he was able to devote almost the whole of his time to thinking. The partner who interviewed me for the job told me that they preferred it that way, and on no account was I to bother Sir Hector with mundane business matters.

Sir Hector Botulus would often start thinking as early as eleven o'clock in the morning and carry on right through lunch without even a break for a sandwich. In the afternoons he would go to his club for a couple of hours, and then he would reappear in the office around five o'clock for a quick think before the chauffeur drove him home.

When I look back on those months which I spent with Sir Hector, I often kick myself at the chance I missed – the chance of learning from him, I mean. There was a man who had developed the art of meditation to a point which has seldom been matched, and yet I, his Personal Assistant, could find nothing better to do than give myself up to idle and irrelevant pursuits around the office. In the morning I would go through the mail with his secretary and dictate the replies for her to sign on his behalf. In the afternoons I would annotate the Association reports and paste up his press cuttings in a big folder. I even urged the partners to let me attend board meetings on his behalf. I said it might ease his load and give him a better idea of what had gone on than if he were present himself.

One day a phone call came through from the Westbury Hotel which the secretary passed on to me. It was the President of a huge American liquor group, who said that he had decided to move part of their promotional budget to Britain and he wanted to talk the whole project over with our firm. He said he was not prepared to discuss such a substantial sum of money with anybody less than the Chairman, and could I give him a time when Sir Hector would be free.

When I reported this potential new liquor account to the partners it threw them into a state of alarm. Some of them said there was nothing to lose. Others said it was the thin end of the wedge and if the Chairman started getting involved in the company's business there was no knowing what would become of them all. They even thought of sending the Deputy Chairman along to pose as Sir Hector, but the legal partner advised caution. He said he had heard of something called the Advertising Code of Practice, and although he was sure that gross deception would be perfectly all right there was always the off-chance that somebody might make difficulties.

In the end they agreed .to the meeting with Sir Hector, and they told me to take full notes. They told me it would have to be as early as possible, before Sir Hector had started thinking for the day, and so at ten o'clock the following morning I met the American on the steps to the office and led him into the boardroom to see our Chairman.

The main object of the American President's visit turned out to be the creation of a promotional campaign for a new brand of port which was to be sold in the Caribbean market. The brand name, he said, was to be Surfing.

'Port is the new fun drink in the Caribbean,' he told us seriously. 'Port is beach parties. It is go-go. It is skin-diving and barracuda time. You can drink it long with tonic or ginger. You can mix it. You can bubble it over a whole mountain of olives and tree-ripened limes. You can take it with bourbon ...'

'Or neat,' said Sir Hector suddenly. It was the first utterance he had made in the whole interview.

The President sat up as though shocked. 'Neat?' he said. 'You mean straight, on the rocks?'

'No,' said Sir Hector.

'You mean ... straight? Just – *straight*!' exclaimed our visitor. The idea that you could pour the stuff directly from the bottle without diluting it with anybody else's product seemed to come to him as a revelation. That was the sort of fresh, original thinking that got the British promotion industry its reputation, he told us, and an hour later he went back to his hotel and sent round two cases of Surfing port and a six-figure contract to come up with a 'total promotion concept'. Sir Hector met the consignment in the lobby when he returned from his club in the afternoon, and he announced that he would be handling the account himself. 'Bring the samples to my office,' he said.

From that moment until the point a month later when Sir Hector was lured away to become marketing consultant for our American principals at an undisclosed salary, the partnership was in a state of tension I don't think I have ever seen equalled. The fluted glass panel between the secretary's office and the boardroom became the pivotal point around which the whole company's activities turned. From early morning until the time Sir Hector was driven away each night, hardly a minute passed without one partner or another dropping in to stare with me at the zigzag, distorted image of the Chairman on the pane. Sometimes he could be seen swaying around slightly – contemplating the shape of a bottle, we thought, or perhaps holding the product up to the light to ponder on its colour. At other times he seemed to be totally immobile, often for hours together. Upstairs on the second floor an operations room was established, with copywriters and artmen standing by, ready to jump into action the moment Sir Hector had finalised his ideas.

At the end of a fortnight the partners couldn't wait any longer. They said the anticipation was killing them, and they sent me into the boardroom to find out what the Chairman had hit upon.

Two weeks of continuous thinking had taken its toll of the old man. His eyes were red with lack of sleep, and he was so bound up in his thoughts that he could hardly bring himself to speak. The bottles he had been studying lay around him in heaps.

I stood directly in front of him to make sure he was aware of my presence, and after a minute or two he looked up and gave a grunt of recognition.

'Sir Hector,' I said, 'the partners want to know whether you have identified a total promotion concept for the Surfing Port Account.'

He looked at me in a distant sort of way, as you might look at a pot-plant or a prize-winning documentary, and for a moment I thought I had lost his attention.

Then he spoke:

'Shurfing', said Sir Hector with difficulty. 'The Port of Kingsh.' And with these words he collapsed to the carpet and lay still.

It's all history now, but that slogan 'The Port of Kings' literally conquered the Caribbean fifteen years ago. It was on hoardings and taxis. It was on radio jingles and T.V. commercials. It was even arranged and performed by steel bands to welcome Heads of State at local airports. But unfortunately the most instantaneous effect from my point of view was that it bore Sir Hector away, upwards and onwards to higher things, which meant that my own job came to an end.

'I hope you've learned something while you've been with us,' the administration partner said to me as we shook hands.

'Oh, yes,' I said. But of course I hadn't. Of course it was going to be years and years before the full significance of what I had witnessed really sank home to me.

And if it takes that long to learn it yourself, just think what an uphill struggle I've got convincing a couple of cloth-heads like Fraser and Henry who don't want to listen in the first place.

At this point Penny came in from the next room where she had been ironing Fraser's shirts. She said that hearing our bickering had made her wonder whether she had done the right thing. She said that she had met the De Veres in the village during the afternoon, the new people who have taken over the Hall. They told her they would like to meet us, and could we pick a suitable evening to go round. They weren't thinking of anything elaborate, just champagne cocktails and some light supper, and they wondered whether Fraser and Penny could come, and that handsome friend of Fraser's with the brown hair (Henry identified this as himself), and also that man who seemed to be at a loose end all the time.

Penny said she had accepted for all of us, but seeing that we couldn't agree about one single simple date, perhaps she had better ring up and say No.

(It seems to me that some people have an odd way of issuing invitations nowadays.)

Fraser said that the critical point here was that the invitation had been accepted. How the hell we were going to comply with it was a different matter, but the effort would have to be made. He said that when his honour had been pledged he wasn't prepared to see innocent people like the De Veres let down.

Henry said it was bloody inconvenient, but it didn't do to be stand-offish towards neighbours. 'I suppose we'd better go, hadn't we, T?'

I said I supposed we had. 'The big difference,' I explained to Penny, 'is that this is just one evening, not the best part of a week, which is what will be entailed in a holiday. A week takes more organising.'

'Well, for heaven's sake get on and organise it then,' Penny said, going back to her ironing board.

Fraser lit his pipe.

'You know the trouble with us?' he said. 'The trouble with us is that we are worrying too much about the *time* and not enough about the *place*.' Fraser produces these flashes of sanity occasionally just to amaze his friends. 'We should try lateral thinking,' he said. 'Tackle a different side of the problem and the original obstacles will melt away.'

I suppose it's remarks like this which start the rumours off that Fraser is intelligent. In this instance he wasn't just being sensible, but – as we were to find out within the hour – prophetic.

'To get back to my Lyke Wake Walk idea,' he said. 'I only

suggested *that* to get our brains ticking over. I don't know much about the Lyke Wake myself, but a man in the office said it would be interesting to see it done.'

I said: 'That sounds like a pretty lousy recommendation.' And Henry said he agreed with me. He said the only part of it he approved of was the Walk, and as far as the rest was concerned we could fry him in oil before he would go struggling twenty miles a day along the Lyke Wake – whatever *that* might be – on the say-so of some berk he had never met. He said he had seen too many holidays ruined in that way, and on his calculation 63.8 per cent of all the misery in the world could be attributed to well-intentioned enthusiasts sending weak-minded others off to places they had never seen.

Some people specialised in it, Henry said. In the 50s and 60s – and for all he knew in the 30s and 40s as well – his late uncle Gervase must have been responsible for more wrecked holidays than any man living.

'Why don't you try Bulgaria?' Henry's Uncle Gervase would cry to perfectly innocent bystanders who might be flicking through a brochure about Clacton while waiting for a train. 'Some of the wildest scenery in Europe and all so cheap.' And they would hurry off wondering why on earth the idea had never occurred to them before. And they would fly out to Bulgaria at the earliest possible moment and get themselves trampled underfoot by folk dancers and thrown into jail for swimming without a licence.

Henry said that his Uncle was once approached by some rather ineffectual people called Watson who asked him if he could give them a few tips about a holiday in France. They said that they had never been before, but they heard it was safe now.

'With pleasure,' he said. 'Whereabouts in France are you going?'

'Calais,' they replied. It transpired afterwards that until they spoke to Henry's uncle they thought that France *was* Calais. They hadn't realised that it went on further.

'Calais!' exclaimed their friend scornfully. 'Calais! A fat lot of enjoyment you're going to get out of Calais! Have you thought about the Camargue?'

They said they hadn't. Nor of course had Henry's uncle until that very moment, but that didn't prevent him from talking as though he were the world authority.

In those days, of course, the Camargue was even further off the beaten track than it is now. The landlord of the little hotel that Henry's Uncle Gervase misled the Watsons into staying at couldn't believe his luck at having a pair of foreigners under his roof, and the whole household came out to greet the taxi which trundled them the forty miles from Marseilles.

The Watsons were asked what they would like to eat, and they said some fish and chips would be nice.

'Feeshes tonight!' cried the patron, and the family all hurried indoors and started chopping things up for dinner.

Dinner, when it came, consisted of a species of local water-serpent, plainly cooked in garlic and a clear green sauce. The Watsons couldn't touch a mouthful, and when no one was looking they slid the fish off their plates and into Mrs Watson's handbag.

'You lika ze feeshes?' beamed the hotelier, trapping them on the stairs as they went up to their room. 'Tomorrow I giving you cheeps. My wife's brozzer he gotta one.'

'Oh, really?'

Over the next fortnight the Watsons practically starved. On the second day – true to the landlord's word – a sheep was brought in by raft from a relative's farmhouse on a distant marsh. It was bleating horribly, and that night they were given its brains. The following evening they had a leg of mutton done nice and red and garnished with blackbirds, the night after that some small shellfish which Mr Watson said reminded him of gallstones, and so on.

The nearest village was seven miles, and there was no telephone in the hotel to ring for a taxi. If it hadn't been for a packet of ginger biscuits which Mrs Watson had rolled up in a bath towel before setting out, they would have had to go without nourishment for the whole of their stay.

Apart from the lack of food, disposing of the meals which they didn't eat became a nightmare for the two visitors. In the case of the water-serpents Mr Watson tried to flush his down the lavatory, but it swam back up again and had to be taken out. In the end they took to putting everything into an airtight tin trunk which was part of their luggage. They didn't dare take it back through the customs, and on the morning of their departure they got up early and carried it downstairs – weak with hunger – and dropped it into the water.

Then they came home and told Henry's Uncle Gervase what a marvellous time they'd had.

So Henry said to Fraser that he wasn't prepared to be the raw material for somebody else's holiday experiments.

I said the same.

Fraser said, apropos Henry's story – which incidentally he remarked that he had heard before – he never had any difficulty in eating anything that was offered to *him*.

Henry said he never had any difficulty in eating anything that was offered to him either, and Fraser said that was the key to Henry's problem.

'But,' said Henry, 'it's not likely to be a question of exotic food, but the lack of any food at all that is the trouble with these moorland walks. Food, and what is more important, drink. A drop of the right stuff, if you know what I mean.'

Fraser and I said we knew exactly what Henry meant, and we were grateful to him for pointing it out. We said a water-bottle was all very well in its way, but it was a big mistake to become a slave to the thing. As purists, we said, we regarded the water-bottle as strictly part of one's survival kit. For normal drinking there should be regular sources of refreshment along the way.

Fraser said he had never actually had a *bad* holiday ever, but there was one which he spent in a Temperance hotel on Windermere which had on occasions been distinctly *trying*.

It's an odd thing – I don't know whether you've noticed it – but nobody will ever admit to having a bad holiday. It's one of the little conventions of civilised life, rather like putting 'Dear Sir' on the top of a letter. The person you are writing to may not be 'Dear' at all. He may be the most villainous, time-serving specimen of a self-satisfied poltroon that ever bungled his way to notoriety, but still you call him 'Dear Sir'. That is how the decencies of existence are maintained. And it's the same thing with holidays. I could, if I'd wanted to, have taken Fraser up on his remark about never having had a bad one. I could have asked him some pretty pointed questions about that expedition he made last January when he took Penny and the children skiing in the Cairngorms.

'I hear they're a bit short of snow up there this year,' I had said to him by way of encouragement as they set off. I knew this was true because I have a cousin of sorts who lives quite close to the place, and he sometimes uses the clubhouse to have a drink in the evening.

Two weeks later I had to ring my cousin up about something or other and I asked him how the snow was coming along.

'Terrible,' my cousin said cheerfully. 'Mildest winter we've had up here for years.' (He doesn't ski himself, of course, so he was taking a macabre pleasure in cataloguing the discomfiture of everybody else.)

It seems that for the first week that Fraser and Penny were on holiday it rained a steady, soaking rain with the monotony of a bathroom tap. This gave way by stages to a warm westerly mist, and in due course to sunshine. Not that crisp, cold sunshine with frost on its breath, but a balmy, lethargic affair which brought all the hillsides out in a riot of colour.

It got so bad, my cousin said, that the skiers started to lay bets with each other as to whether there was any snow at all, and they sent a two-day expedition up into the peaks to see if they could spot any. The hotelier, who led the expedition in order to defend his establishment's reputation, came back with a handful of snow in a thermos flask, but the skiers refused to pay out. They said he had manufactured it in the fridge.

When Fraser reappeared at the end of the month I asked him how he had got on.

'Magnificent,' he said. 'Did you get our postcard?'

'Yes,' I said. 'Was it really as snowy as all that?'

'I'll say,' said Fraser with gusto. 'A bit light on the lower slopes for the first few days, which didn't help the beginners. But up above it was perfection. Some of the finest ski-runs in Europe, if you ask me.'

Just then the miracle happened – or rather the answer to Fraser's prophecy. Widget (my wife) and Katrina (Henry's) rang up from home to say that *Blithe Spirit* had been cancelled. Joyce Wingham, the *ex officio* leading lady, had gone down with German measles, and Daphne – the nervous Number Two – thought she might be pregnant and didn't want to risk it.

The news was received with quiet satisfaction at our end.

'Have *you* any idea where we ought to go, T?' Henry asked.

'I have it on good authority,' I replied, 'that Offa's Dyke is the greatest monument to the Dark Ages still visible in Europe.'

'Ah,' said Henry. 'And how is it off for pubs?'

I said: 'My last remark was not just spoken at a venture. It is a quotation from the foundation textbook *Forty Good Pubs on Offa's Dyke*.'

'Aha!' said Henry and Fraser together.

It was getting on for ten o'clock, and Fraser called through to Penny to ask her how supper was coming along.

'It's ready now,' Penny called back.

A glance of intelligence passed between the three of us.

'Look, Darling,' said Fraser, becoming ingratiating in a rather routine sort of a way, 'would you like to keep the supper going for a while? I think we had better slip down to the Woolpack for a brief recap before we begin.'

'In point of fact,' Penny told us as we tugged on our wellingtons, 'I never put the supper on at all. I am starting now. Shall I expect you back at, say, 11.15?'

# 2

# Thinking it Through

'This expedition of ours,' said Fraser as we walked along the road to the Woolpack, 'will have to be mulled over in some detail. It's going to be just like *Three Men in a Boat.'*

'Except of course there won't be a boat,' said Henry.

'Except for that,' said Fraser.

'And also there won't be a dog,' said Henry. 'Remember, the real title is *Three Men in a Boat to say Nothing of the Dog*. We have no dog.'

'Thank God for that,' said Fraser.

Mrs Blenkiron keeps a very decent pint. It is cool and chewy and it focuses the mind quite wonderfully.

Henry said we ought to discuss the pros and cons of camping.

I said No. Not that I had any particular aversion to camping, but the conditions needed to be right for it. Camping with Henry, I may tell you, is a humiliating experience for everybody – except for Henry of course. Fraser says that in gastronomic terms it is rather like sitting down to a sausage roll on the beach and then finding that the Aga Khan is picnicking beside you.

'Now we are really going to live rough,' Henry tells his wife and children as they load every imaginable aid to comfort into the Volvo for him on the night before the expedition. 'You packed the Malvern Water, did you, Annie, and the spare battery for my toothbrush?'

'Yes, papa.'

And if you happen to be passing Henry's house next morning on the way to getting a few groceries, you stop in amazement at the sight of all the luggage piled up on his roof-rack, and you begin wondering what it is you could possibly have forgotten that makes your load so much lighter than his. And when you get into the town you phone up your wife and make her read over the list of items to you again and again, and the two of you get wild with each other trying to think what you have missed off.

Then, after a while, you start to imagine that it is Henry who must have taken leave of his senses, and the idea strikes you as extremely funny.

'Poor old Henry,' you say. 'He's really dropped a clanger this time. He won't get all that kit erected in a month of Sundays. What a laugh we'll have when we see him struggling with that lot.'

And when you set out to drive to the camp-site in the afternoon the long journey is lightened by the thought that Henry will be stumbling round in the darkness when you will be safely tucked up in your sleeping-bags. Towards evening a drizzle comes on and that only seems to make the joke all the funnier.

The camp-site is crowded, but you manage to find a little niche for yourselves between a colony of ecumenical Germans and a large modern 'canvas home' which is so sophisticated it seems to have double-glazing. You start to unroll your tent, and the very moment you do so it dawns on you what you have forgotten – the groundsheet. Not only that, but you suddenly remember that you tucked the instructions for assembling the tent inside the groundsheet the last time you used it a couple of years ago so you'd know where to find them.

By the time dusk falls you have got the back half of the tent in place, but the front refuses to stand up. An irritating man in a mackintosh who has been watching you unblinkingly for the last twenty minutes tells you that it reminds him of a pantomime horse where the head-end has gone on strike, and he goes off to have his supper laughing at his own feeble joke.

In desperation you decide to take a tea-break and you huddle together round the methylated stove in the part of the tent which is actually standing and peer out from the soggy canvases into the rain.

'No sign of Henry,' you say to each other, clutching around for some sort of silver lining in the whole affair. 'What a mess he'll be in! Why, he's got hours of work ahead of him – even if he can find a site, which seems unlikely.'

And then, just as you are talking, there is a revving of an engine and a pip-pip-pip, and Henry has parked his little red car beside you and is winding down the window.

'Having a spot of bother?' he enquires.

'Bother?' you say, beginning to smile to yourselves for the first time in ages. 'Bother? Oh no, *we're* all right. Just this moment arrived, as a matter of fact. We always like to have a quick cup of tea before we get really started. Why don't the lot of us meet up for a chat in half an hour or so when we're all finished?'

'That's the style,' says Henry blandly. 'Couldn't get away in time to put the tent up myself, so I sent Katrina and the girls on ahead to sort it out for me. They're staying with an aunt of mine for the night. Camping's no activity for women. They can't take the rough-and-tumble.' And so saying he opens the door-flap of the canvas home next to you, flicks on an automatic hurricane lamp inside, reaches down his bedroom slippers, and subsides into an easy chair where he can watch you for the next two hours through his enormous picture-window.

The sight of Henry staring out at you unnerves you. While you were drinking your tea you had gradually realised that the long pole which is supporting the back of the tent ought really to be at the front, but now you are damned if you are going to change it round with him watching. Instead you mackle up a new front pole out of odd lengths of rod which are meant to go round the top of the walls, with the result that the sides of the canvas sag inwards like a deflated balloon. To keep them apart you tie one wall up to an overhanging branch and the other to the top of the German tent. The Germans hear you at work and they all come out and play their guitars at you and give you copies of the Bible, which you tell them you will read later.

Towards eleven o'clock Henry comes shambling over and asks you whether you would like to join him for some pâté and toast before turning in.

'*Pâté*!' you exclaim with a distracted laugh. 'Not for us, thank you very much. We've eaten. We were so quick about it you probably didn't notice. We just heated up a can of stew and gobbled it down in a flash. Nothing like a nice early night when you're camping, we always say.'

Then you crawl inside the darkened folds and feel about in the wet grass for a bag of tomatoes.

That is what camping with Henry is like.

Fraser said that nowadays you could hire special lightweight tents for walkers, and provided we got a single three-man job, Henry's natural excesses would be kept in check. 'Not that we'll be under canvas every night, mark you,' he said. 'But it will give us the option to sleep out if we have to.'

I said, 'What about the car? If we leave it at one end of the Dyke, it'll be in the wrong place when we want to come home.'

Fraser said he'd already thought of that. He said you could bet your bottom dollar the girls would start yelling for a holiday too. 'They can go to Wales on a coach and pick up the car at the other end,' he said. 'That will keep them quiet. They can use it to drive round Ludlow Castle and so forth and drop it off for us when the holiday is over.'

I said that perhaps they wouldn't want to go round Ludlow Castle, but Fraser said that was nonsense. He said that in his experience all women wanted to go round Ludlow Castle and that any who didn't must be suffering from a damaged personality and weren't running true to type. He said that most of them wanted to watch performances of Milton's *Comus* while they were there as well, but that wasn't an absolutely fundamental characteristic of the species.

He said the journey to North Wales would take three hours. Henry said it would take three and a half. I said five.

I don't know why it is, but some of the wildest exaggerations on this earth arise over the perfectly measurable question of how long it takes to get from one place to another. I sometimes think that if all the anglers who stand around in fishing hotels telling grisly half-truths to each other were to go down to Silverstone or Le Mans once a year and mingle with the motoring fraternity their capacity for barefaced lying would be very much improved.

I had a friend once who had been brought up in Sweden where the motoring code is so rigid that it's best not to drive at all unless you have a police escort. My friend – his name, I think, was Djerk Hamstrung or something of that sort – came from a small provincial town where everybody spoke the truth all of the time and ate open sandwiches. Then, when he was about twenty-seven and beginning to grow up, his father sent him to stay with some people in Chipping Sodbury so he could see a bit of the world.

This was before the days of motorways, and my friend hired the latest little Ford to drive round all the important centres like Banbury and Stow-on-the-Wold.

Now, as it happened, the people my friend was staying with were working farmers who had to spend most of their time at point-to-points and eating-houses with others in the same line of occupation, and after he had been with them for a few weeks they told him one evening that they were going over to Newmarket the following day. They were going on business, they said, and would be away for a few nights, but he would be most welcome to pop over and join them if he cared to make it a day trip.

'What sort of speed do you think you'll average on the Newmarket run?' said one of the farmers as they stood at the bar.

My Swedish friend knew the geography of England quite well from his schooldays, and he considered the question carefully. 'I should think,' he said, 'that I could manage about thirty-two miles an hour.'

Then all his farming friends and all their friends fell about laughing. They said they always knew the English had a sense of humour, but they never realised the Swedes could be so deliciously droll. The barman produced a piece of paper and asked him to write the remark down, so he could pin it up behind the counter for other clients to read, and an old gentleman of about eighty at the end of the bar, who everybody thought was some sort of standing ornament, suddenly woke up and said, 'What d'yer fill the tank with – lager?' And this made them roar all the louder and start banging on the tables, and the old gentleman seemed to have some sort of fit, he found it so funny, and he had to be taken out into the night air and given brandy.

In the end the party all settled on sixty-two miles an hour as the fair mean for the trip, and they drove away and went to bed, saying they'd never had such an amusing evening in their lives.

My friend got up early the next morning and made his own breakfast. He had asked to be *woken* early, but everybody else thought that was still part of his joke, so they just lay in their rooms and wondered whether their men had started milking the cows. Over his coffee my friend studied a road atlas to see if there was some mysterious route to Newmarket that he hadn't considered, but the more he pored over the pages the more puzzled he became as to why he was supposed to have got it so wrong.

Eventually, being a carefully reared young man, he decided that there was nothing for it but to stick to what he had originally thought. He set out by the most straightforward route, and stopped in Bedford for a quick snack and a stroll round. In Huntingdon he filled up with petrol, and he turned into the carpark at Newmarket just twenty minutes before the first race.

The other members of the party all appeared one after the other at around quarter to four. They had come by a variety of routes, but it seemed that each one of them had been held up for hours by a quite untypical series of traffic jams and burst tyres. If you didn't count that, they said, they must have averaged seventy miles an hour each. They said that if it hadn't been for their skill as drivers and their detailed knowledge of the country they might never have got there at all. They said the racecourse was particularly empty that day, which only proved that the ordinary, plodding motorists hadn't managed to win through.

So I said we would start early, and if we found we were ahead of ourselves we could break our journey on the way. Henry said that would suit him fine, because he was planning to bring his binoculars for bird-watching.

By the time Mrs Blenkiron was calling 'Time', our schemes were beginning to shape up nicely. I should explain that the calling of 'Time' in our neck of the woods is a cherished custom which we wouldn't for the world see discontinued. As a practice it is of unknown antiquity, and it is always accompanied by Mr Turner, the village policeman, moving his panda car from the front of the pub to the back. This is an important feature of the ritual, and when Mr Turner comes in again we show our respect for the ceremony by standing for a moment with our heads bowed before ordering another round of drinks.

Fraser said: 'We won't write down what we're going to take with us. The size of the boot will make sure we don't carry too much. What we *will* write down, however, is the things we must do before we leave.' Fraser said it had been well observed – whether by Winston Churchill or by himself he couldn't for the moment recall – that it was better not to travel at all than arrive at the other end and remember that you had left the cat locked up in the master bedroom.

Henry got out some paper and a chewed-off biro.

'Mrs Drabble,' said Fraser, 'tell her to discontinue dusting the mantelpiece for two weeks.

'That's all that woman ever does,' he added. 'What Penny sees in her I can't imagine. If I could get one pound fifty per foot of mantelpiece per week I'd retire from active work straight away.'

Henry said what about notifying the police that we were going, but Fraser said it was a waste of time. He said we could leave that aspect of the business to him, and by the time we left the pub he would make sure we didn't get any burglars while we were away.

After ten minutes of thinking and Henry sucking at his pen to colourful effect and writing in a big round hand, we had our list of things to do before departing fairly battened down.

It read:

Mrs Drabble: not to dust mantelpiece
Ditto Mrs Hutch and Mrs Soames
Milkman
Newspapers
Tell GPO to continue not delivering the mail
Lawns: cut savagely with intent to blight future growth
Ditto Roses
Fraser's answering machine: leave smooth infuriating message
for callers saying he will be back in five minutes.
Penny's hens: leave 7 days' supply of fowl food to
last until our return.

Henry said that this last item was ridiculous. He said you couldn't expect the hens to measure out their daily rations and feed themselves systematically. They would only gorge like elephants for the first two days and then go hungry for the rest of the holiday.

Fraser said that that was their own look-out and it would teach them a lesson for the future. He said the economic truth was that it wasn't the going away, it was the settling up afterwards with kennels and catteries and sweet old ladies who promised to keep an eye on your geraniums that drove the average holiday-maker to the brink of ruin.

He said that when he was first married Penny brought with her – possibly as part of her dowry, he couldn't say – a pig called Esterhazy. He said he knew in advance that Penny's family were dotty about animals, so he didn't think anything more about it except when the wind was in the east and wafting in a direct line from the pigsty to the house.

When the time came round for their first summer holiday together Fraser suddenly thought of the pig. He asked Penny what they ought to do about it, and she said that old Mr Arkle from the village was supposed to have a way with animals and perhaps he could keep an eye on it for them.

Mr Arkle duly came up on the morning of Fraser's departure. He was old and lacking intelligence and inarticulate, and he seemed just right for the job. After a series of initial misunderstandings the work was agreed on at an hourly rate, and Fraser and Penny drove away.

Fraser says that within a minute of setting out on holiday he had completely dismissed the cost of Mr Arkle's labours from his thoughts. It seemed to him that whatever it came to it would be so little as not to be worth bothering about. In his mind's eye he imagined that Mr Arkle would spend about twenty minutes with the animal each day, giving it here a bucket of water, there a panful of potatoes. Then the pig and Mr Arkle might have a short chat as between equals for a minute or two, and both would go their separate ways.

Just what made up Mr Arkle's final bill of £68.50 Fraser never really found out. The crumpled invoice, with its single sum of money written in the middle, appeared oddly to be the work of several hands. But since no words accompanied the solitary figure, Fraser had to go and ask Mr Arkle to give him a breakdown. After several weeks of probing Fraser finally came to the conclusion that – apart from two sacks of expensive meal and a badger-hair pig brush – he was paying in the main for a series of cultural conversations between man and beast that must have extended to several hours a day.

Ever after that, Fraser said, he has made it a rule in his household that there are to be no hidden extras in the cost of any holiday: no hidden extras, and no policemen turning up at the house three nights after you've got back and shining arc-lamps in at you through the bedroom window, and then checking in their notebooks to see why they've got the wrong date, and asking you to identify yourself.

'The way to deal with burglars,' Fraser said, 'is as follows. All you have to do is to say "Yes" in loud resonant tones in answer to every question that I feed you. Clear?'

'Yes,' said Henry and I pretty loudly.

'Right,' yelled Fraser. 'So that's our holiday fixed. We set out – what, in three weeks' time?'

'Yes,' shouted Henry.

'And we'll be gone, I should think, for a good couple of weeks?'

'Yes,' I said.

'What'll you do with the Alsatian, Henry – put it in the kennels?'

'Yes,' said Henry, 'I always do.'

'And you'll give the gardener a fortnight off, will you, T?"

'I will,' I shouted.

'Fine! Then we we'll have a last pint before we go please, Mrs Blenkiron.'

'Now *that*,' said Fraser as we strolled back, 'is foolproof crime prevention. The only bother you'll have is that two or three strange characters will turn up after you've got back and mutter something sheepishly about gravelling your drive.'

It took us rather a long time to make our way home. In fact, if we hadn't been in the capable hands of Fraser, I could have sworn that he led us past the same house twice. Fraser said Nonsense. He said that the trouble with the age of the car was that people had lost all sense of the time it takes to make a journey on foot. He had noticed this himself more than once, particularly after dark. He said that sometimes when he stepped out of the Woolpack in the late evening the stroll home seemed to take almost twice as long as the outward journey; so much so that if he didn't know better, he might have thought that he'd set off in the wrong direction.

The church clock was striking half past midnight as we turned in at Fraser's gate. Penny was in bed, and a cold and distinctly frazzled-looking mixed grill was waiting for us in the kitchen. We fell on the charred components manfully.

'It's a funny thing about my wife,' Fraser told us. 'Penny can cook perfectly well when she sets her mind to it. But when it comes to timing she hasn't the first idea.'

# 3

# Getting it Together

That was Sunday night. Or, if you want to be pernickety, Monday morning.

We decided to leave after an early breakfast on the Wednesday, and since that gave us just two days to get ourselves organised we adopted a plan of campaign.

Henry's house was made the collecting point for all the paraphernalia. Henry said that was logical, because we'd be going in his Volvo. Fraser said it was even more logical than that because it meant that Henry could lie back at home and rootle through the various bits of gear that he (Fraser) and I brought in.

I rang a camping shop for a lightweight tent and three hiking-frames. Fraser checked the coach times for the girls' journey to Wales, and one way and another we pushed on our preparations with vigour and common sense.

Fraser and I had a shock on the Tuesday afternoon. We had gone into the town together to pick up the groceries and the camping equipment, and as we strolled between the two shops we were talking in a desultory sort of way about whether we mightn't be overloading ourselves.

The camping shop in Milford is one of those vast, shadowy, professional-looking places which have all changed their names from things like *Bodger and Perkins: Canvases and Ropemakers* into *Living Off The Land* and *Great Outdoors*.

Fraser and I walked in, and I said to the proprietor, 'We have come to collect the tent and three walking-frames which I rang you about yesterday.'

'Ah yes,' said the man without glancing up. 'That's the light-weight Matthew-Walker. I'll just finish this gent and then I'll be right with you, my friend.'

I looked at Fraser in some surprise. Fraser looked at me. We both looked behind us. Apart from the two of us and the proprietor there was nobody else in the shop.

We peered into the darker recesses, but there was no sign of life. The canvas jackets and sou'westers were hanging bulky and motionless on a rail at the farther end. The shop window was still as a photograph.

After a while Fraser started strolling about in curiosity, peering inside the lids of trunks and snapping his fingers at the faces of all the plaster models to see if he could make them blink. I put my head into a small blue tent, but it was empty.

All this while the proprietor seemed to be carrying on a conversation with himself, ticking things off on a pad as he prattled along. 'Spare boot-studs,' he would say. 'Two packets of those. Laces – two. Tent-pegs – now we had the hardened steel type, didn't we? – yes. So it's four boxes of D173B – always best to have the proper job.'

After a while Fraser and I just perched ourselves on a heap of sleeping-bags and watched him. It seemed such a harmless eccentricity that we were disappointed when he finally got to the bottom of the page and started adding it up. 'What a pity,' we said to ourselves. 'We were just beginning to enjoy this. So much better than half the stuff you get on the goggle-box nowadays.'

'There we are, sir. This is your docket,' said the proprietor eventually, maintaining his illusion to the last. 'We'll charge it to your private account.' And so saying he tore the top page off his pad and stuffed it into a pile of knapsacks and bedrolls that was propped against the front of the counter.

'Thanks very much,' said the pile of knapsacks and bedrolls. Then, in a most astonishing way, the pile seemed to pick itself up and started moving towards the door.

'Nice day for a walk anyway,' shouted the knapsacks and bedrolls back over its shoulder as it went.

'Mind how you go now,' exclaimed the proprietor cheerfully.

Fraser said it was the sight of the mickey-mouse feet trundling like clockwork beneath all the apparatus that first told him that there was some form of humanity strapped inside it.

For my part I never saw the feet, so I had to wait for the whole bundle to stagger sideways into a pillar before I realised there was a man there. Huddersfield-born, I would say, and judging by the choice of words a man of no mean education.

We asked the proprietor if the man was part of the British Trans-Polar Expedition, and the proprietor said, No, he was a chap called Copple who was off for a weekend's rambling in Bedfordshire.

'A very good customer of mine Mr Copple,' he said, suddenly alert like a missionary or estate agent. 'Deep into survival economics – it makes so much sense when you think about it.'

Fraser said, as we drove back, that it would be a good warning for us not to take too much.

We found Henry at home – hard at work entertaining the girls to tea and madeira cake. He was surrounded by a sea of packages and bundles, most of which I suspect he had put there himself as necessities for the trip.

Widget said we'd never be able to carry all that lot on our backs and Henry said we certainly would. Katrina said it depended what you meant by 'carry'. In the sense that it could all be piled on to us somehow to score an entry in the *Guinness Book of Records* she couldn't deny that it might be technically possible. But we had to think of the practical aspects. She had read somewhere that tortoises which rolled over in the desert were never able to get back upright again and died horribly under the howling blue sky.

Fraser suggested that the practical way of finding out was for the three of us to get changed into our walking clothes and then strap ourselves into the back-packs to see how comfortable we were. This seemed like a good idea and it didn't take long – at least not so far as putting on the clothes was concerned.

For myself I had been rather waiting for a chance to change. I had given a good deal of quiet thought to what I was going to wear and I expected the effect to be rather striking. A gentleman on holiday, it seemed to me, should appear to be just that – a gentleman, on holiday. Not for him the leatherette plimsolls and padded anorak of the bogus professional. From the wardrobe in my den I had selected a pair of my uncle's old plus-fours woven from a particularly tasteful pinkish tweed, hairy stockings and army boots, and a new lightweight colonial jacket in beige denim which I had snapped up at the sales.

Fraser and I met at the top of the stairs. 'Good God!' he exclaimed when he saw me.

I gave him a look of disgust. For some mysterious reason he himself appeared to be dressed out of the scourings of the garden shed.

Our entry certainly caused a sensation. As we came in, Widget dropped a saucer with a bang, and Penny broke out into a nervous laugh and had to be calmed down with a glass of water.

Just at that moment Henry opened the door. For a second I thought we had been joined by a bumblebee. Then I realised that that couldn't be so. The middle part of his body from the waist to the knee was swathed in black nylon knickerbockers with a yellow zig-zag stripe careering up the thigh. He had no stockings, but an enormous pair of mountain boots made him look as if he was walking on sucker-pads. His headgear was a luminous long-peaked golf cap.

Katrina said: 'Let us be serious for a moment. As a piece of contemporary theatre or a trio of lunatics in a Christmas charades party your appearances could not be faulted. However, you are supposed to be walking through the countryside and I am anxious to avoid a terrorist incident. The inhabitants of the Welsh borders are a simple people, and to speak frankly I am not sure that they will get the joke. They may see your arrival – and I can't say that I could blame them – as an invasion of privacy, possibly even a sketch for a BBC satirical programme. I can't speak for anyone else, but as far as Henry is concerned if he doesn't make this journey in a Guernsey sweater and jeans he can look for other accommodation when he gets back.'

Widget said the same, and Penny said that provided Fraser could spare her forty-eight hours and the money for seven reels of thread and a new washing machine she thought she could get him looking respectable before he set out.

So it was back upstairs again, change, and back down again feeling disgruntled. But the mood didn't last long. The sight of the back-packs and all the equipment soon had Henry brightening up.

Henry loves equipment. It goes so well with his indolent

nature. In fact, if it weren't for the warm-hearted action of his friends in steering him out on walks and cycle-rides and on to tennis courts, he could cheerfully sit at home all day just playing with the gadgets and instruction books he has got himself without bothering about the physical side of the thing at all.

Take these hiking-frames, for instance. There they all were, neatly folded away into their plastic wallets, each containing its delicious bundle of tubes and straps, to say nothing of the little packets of wing-nuts and snap-on clips. Then there was the instruction leaflet with its picture of a gypsy-eyed *campeuse* beckoning you in no fewer than six languages to plunge inside and start assembling all the bits and pieces. '*Assemblage actuated with facility*,' was the way she expressed herself in the English version – and I must say you can't put it plainer than that.

You've noticed, have you, the odd thing about instruction leaflets, that however arduous the task it always seems to be taken in hand by a woman in the few minutes she can spare between slipping into her swimsuit and dashing down to the beach. I suppose it is all to do with the march of progress. There was a time when grown men would make heavy weather of a simple job like re-aligning a land-drain or taking the cylinder-head off a combine harvester. Today this sort of thing can be done quite easily while your nail varnish is drying.

So, with Henry and Fraser and me doing the operation, just think what a doddle it would be.

We each opened our plastic packet and laid all the pieces out in front of us. Yummy yummy.

I had one piece less than Henry, and Fraser had a piece which was a different shape from any of ours, but Henry told us both to stop griping. He said the whole thing would be covered in the instructions.

'*One*,' he said, reading attentively from the page. '*Overplace bracket A at Arm 6*.'

We did as we were told.

'*Two. Samely Bracket B, Arm 7*.'

Quite.

'*Three. Proform unique compaction*.'

Now I freely admit it was probably here that we went wrong, though I will say of my own compaction that it was certainly unique. As a result of it, Bracket A quite capriciously sheared itself off and lay on the carpet with its feet in the air, looking for a rôle, so to speak. By comparison with mine, Fraser and Henry's compactions were weak-kneed, lily-livered affairs which didn't seem to advance the cause of back-pack assembly by a single step.

We all stopped and looked at the picture. Then we tried again.

After that we tried again.

It seemed to us – and this is why we gave so much attention to the compaction proforming process – that Stage 3 was an important step in terms of the overall assembly. After Stage 3, you see, the girl in the illustration had quite clearly got herself something which was the recognisable skeleton of a hiking-frame. And it not only looked right, but it obviously hung together, because as soon afterwards as Stage 4 she could be observed kneeing it in the groin in order to '*sustain curves for shapement formation*' – a fairly painful moment for the frame, by the look of things.

Now *our* frames weren't like that at all. When you picked our frames up they all just tumbled apart on to the floor and rolled about in little pieces as though they wanted us to play spillikins with them.

'Look,' said Henry after the fifth attempt at compaction. 'You two take the picture and I'll do the action bit. Then you watch and tell me what' – he nearly said 'what the bloody flaming hell' but he didn't – 'you tell me *what* I am doing wrong. Ready ... Go!'

Fraser and I got it at once. In a flash. No doubt about it at all.

'You're not grinning properly,' we said. 'Look at the drawing, man. Behold the wench swathed in smiles from ear to ear. Subliminal stuff. We're in the realms of the occult, Henry old lad – mind-over-matter and all that.'

'Think of Tibet,' Fraser added encouragingly.

I must say that, for somebody who is as out of touch with the occult as Henry normally is, the results of this advice were far better than we could have expected. Briefly remarking 'Sod Tibet!' – a well-known greeting in the Himalayas – Henry put his foot on Arm 6 as it sat there overplacing Bracket A and scrunched it down into firm contact with the carpet. I couldn't see the grin on his face of course because he had his back to me;

but, judging by the outcome, it must have been one of those big wide dreamy ones of his which he lets loose from time to time. Result? Compaction. Good, old-fashioned, unique compaction – and marvellously proformed with it. Absolutely as per diagram.

Fraser and I said that now we'd seen how it was done we'd let Henry carry on to the finish. We said we didn't want to steal his thunder by coming up with half-baked imitations of our own.

Henry got on pretty well after that. He formated the shapement curves for Stage 4, and then he hooked on Brackets C to E and overplaced them at Arms 2 to 5. Then he got the straps in place and extended all the buckles so they fitted round his tummy. And then, just as he was about to break into his broadest grin, he caught the eye of Fraser and me looking out at him over a Tibetan peak of packs and packages.

'That's all the stuff we've got to carry, is it?' he said nervously.

'No,' we assured him. 'It's all the stuff *you've* got to carry. It is your third, traveller.'

'Either that,' I said, 'or you can hire a porter.'

We laid the frame down on the floor and tied the bundles on for him. Henry said there was a proper way of 'dressing' a back-pack so that everything had its place. But we said we would overlook it if he wasn't properly dressed on this occasion. 'It's just for the experiment,' we said.

Henry said there was a proper way of putting on a back-pack too, and we said come on show us. So he knelt down on his left knee, and after a brief search for one of the shoulder-straps which had concealed itself inside the rolled up sleeping-bags, we finally got him saddled into the thing. Then Fraser and I strolled away towards the mantelpiece and started eating cake, while Henry went very quiet and pink in the face.

Fraser and I watched him with keen interest. Exactly what Henry was doing kneeling on the floor going pink in the face we didn't know. I thought myself that he might be doing some exercises – a silent muscle-flexing routine which we would all have to go through every time we set out. Fraser commented through a mouthful of crumbs that it looked more spiritual than that. He thought perhaps he was reciting something – a poem by Landor perhaps, or a code of conduct called *The Happy Hiker's Dos and Don'ts*.

We found out from Henry himself. 'Here! Help me up, can't

you?' he spluttered out at last in something between a gasp and a roar. 'This load's too darned heavy to stand in.'

We levered him to his feet.

Slowly and smoothly, like a trombone, the tubes of Henry's hiking-frame slid apart under the weight of the bundles. It wasn't exactly a dramatic moment – it was too long-drawn-out for that – but it was a moment of rich sadness. A captain going down with his ship must wear much the same expression as Henry did when his bundle of packages subsided softly on to the carpet.

Fraser said it had been an interesting experiment – unsuccessful but interesting – and no doubt we would be trying it again. In the meantime, however – till we got it right – he hoped we wouldn't mind if he used a rather less modern method of carrying luggage from A to B. Like so many old-fashioned ideas, it was quite amazingly effective: it was called a suitcase.

The girls were sleeping at our house, and we were sleeping at Henry's. The girls had said it would be better that way because then they wouldn't rouse us when they got up to make breakfast. We said it would be more of a case of our not wanting to rouse them, and they said Yes, sorry – that was what they'd meant.

So they drove away, and Henry and Fraser and I wandered into the kitchen, and grilled ourselves some herrings which Katrina had thoughtfully laid on for us. Then we sat round the table and drank beer.

'This time tomorrow,' I said, 'we will be on the Welsh Marches.'

'Why do they call 'em Marches?' said Fraser reflectively.

'Because they *march* beside us,' I said. 'Simple as that.'

The evening was clear and it was a night of stars. Far off, all those leagues along the sky, the seven lamps of Orion hung like a guardian warrior over the hills of Dyfed. Fraser drew at his pipe and spoke in a low voice:

> The winds out of the west land blow,
> My friends have breathed them there;
> Warm with the blood of lads I know
> Comes east the sighing air.

It fanned their temples, filled their lungs,
Scattered their forelocks free;
My friends made words of it with tongues
That talk no more to me.

'You must still be hungry,' Henry said. 'Sorry we've run out of herrings. How about a slice of toast?'

# 4

# Starting if Off

We set off at eleven the next morning and drove right across the middle of England.

Actually it wasn't quite like that. The idea had been to rise at about 6.30 or 7, have a substantial breakfast of kippers and toast – it must be something to do with Katrina's Norwegian ancestry that herrings in one form or another seem to be the staple diet when you're staying with Henry – and then load the car up with the bits and pieces and drive purposefully off in search of adventure.

What actually happened was that Henry suddenly burst into the downstairs room where I was dozing fitfully on my palliasse and snatched up the telephone. You know how it is when you're sleeping. I suppose if it had gone on ringing for another five minutes or so I could have identified it as the phone and answered it myself. As it was, I had formed the perfectly reasonable impression that somebody was shearing a sheep over by the fireplace, so I didn't think anything more about it.

Henry was in his pyjamas, or rather bulging out of them in all directions.

'Hooizzit? Wassamatter?' he said in his best switchboard manner. 'Oh it's you. Ye ... N ... I ... Of course we ... don't be ridicul ... Well, if you want to do that for us of course we'd be very grateful, darling. Ra ... ther. We're just finishing off. Give us – what, let's say half an hour. No – forty minutes at the most. Aha ha ... No, my poppet, we were just out packing the car ... All right. Bye then. Bye.

'Blast!' he said, smashing the receiver down and whisking round. 'It's ten o'clock and the girls are coming over to clear up after we've gone. We'd better get our skates on.'

I did the kippers in a jug, while Henry and Fraser threw all the packages into the car. Then we gulped down the breakfast and zoomed off, leaving Fraser's razor on the washbasin in the bathroom. Fraser said he wouldn't buy another – he'd grow a beard instead.

The less said about the middle part of England the better – and I don't mean that in the way you think I mean it. The good thing about splendid Midland towns like Market Harborough and Melton Mowbray is that people don't really know they exist. They aren't dramatic enough for them. British Rail has had a half-hearted go at giving them a tourist image by opening a Shires Restaurant in St. Pancras station, but since they never manage to lure any tourists to St. Pancras in the first place the gesture is largely ineffectual. The result is that these rolling pasture-laden counties, with their thick thorn hedges and their solid prosperous villages, have been left to themselves, and much better they are for it. So, whenever anybody says to me 'Leicestershire – let me see now, that's Birmingham way, isn't it?', I say 'Yes', and I utter a prayer that they will go off and tell their friends that Leicestershire is really part of Greater Birmingham, so they can dismiss it from their minds and carry on spending their holidays in the Lake District and the Norfolk broads.

We made an unscheduled stop at Lichfield. It was meant to be a five-minute stop, and it lasted an hour and a half.

What happened was this. Fraser, who was driving, said he was fed up with motorways and he wanted to take a quick look at Lichfield Cathedral.

Henry said he was fed up with motorways too, but he didn't think Lichfield Cathedral was necessarily the cure.

Fraser said it was the birthplace of Dr Johnson, and Henry said 'What, the Cathedral?'

So Fraser just turned off at Junction 10 and drove us straight into Lichfield and put the car in a multi-storey carpark and led us out through a side-door into the Cathedral close, with me looking alert and intelligent and Henry grumbling like an appendix.

We had just got as far as the porch and were adjusting the sanctimonious expressions on our faces when the South Door slid open, as if by its own accord, and a venerable prodnose stuck his head out. He had the look of a man who has an unpleasant duty to perform and intends to enjoy every minute of it.

The following conversation ensued:

*Venerable Prodnose (aggressively)*: 'Yes?'
*Fraser*: 'We want to look round the Cathedral.'
*V.P.*: 'No visitors allowed now. It's three o'clock.'
*Fraser*: 'And what's so special about three o'clock?'
*V.P.*: 'Evensong, see. Cathedral's closed for evensong.'
*Fraser*: 'You mean – or should mean, I presume – the Cathedral's *open* for evensong.'
*(Venerable Prodnose pauses for about 20 seconds of mental constipation, then goes back to his script)*
*V.P.*: 'Cathedral's closed for evensong.'

We sized the figure up. No Verger or Sexton he. Just one of those mouldering lookers-on that one finds around museums and ecclesiastical architecture waiting for an opportunity to put their oar in.

Fraser tried reasoning with the man. He said that though no doubt it was normal for evensong to be sung to an empty nave it didn't necessarily follow that it *had* to be so. Every now and then – perhaps once in an old pest's lifetime – a party of people would turn up at a Cathedral door who were actually prepared to endure an evensong – might even get a morose sort of pleasure out of the thing.

This idea didn't seem to tally with the man's own experience. He didn't say anything. He just stood there blinking reflectively in the most negative way he could muster, and then ducked inside and started to close the door.

He started to close the door, but he didn't close it, because Henry slid forward and put his foot in it so it bounced back.

Prodnose's head came out again.

Henry said: 'Be a good chap and let us in.' He added that we had come all the way from Essex just to go to evensong at Lichfield, and the authorities wouldn't want us to come away disappointed, now, would they?

There's something very persuasive about Henry at times. You wouldn't expect it of a man who weighs in at over fifteen stone, but he can be so delicate and charming that people just seem to melt in front of him. I was particularly struck by the very human and vice-like way he clamped his hand on to the other's own as it gripped the door handle. Then he gave a squeeze.

I've never seen such a transformation as appeared on that interfering busybody's face. One minute he couldn't see the thing from our point of view at all, the next sympathy and understanding dawned. He said that, since we mentioned it, there were one or two special pews just above the choir, and would we rather be on the Decani side or the Cantoris? He said he apologised for not seeing at a glance the sort of gentlemen we were, but so many people who came to the Cathedral nowadays just didn't have the Christian spirit at all, and as far as he was concerned they could go away and boil their faces.

So we sat on the Cantoris side and we heard Stanford in G and a fine In Nomine by Thomas Tomkins, beautifully sung. After the anthem the officiating cleric tried his hand at some extempore prayer – so it wasn't all roses – and then we slipped out as fast as we decently could behind the choir.

As we strolled back across the close to the carpark, Fraser said: 'Extempore prayer in the C. of E. is rather like ordering a well-done steak in France.' (Pause.) 'Is it not *well* done, but one is surprised to find it done at all.'

Henry said that as jokes go it was lousy, but Fraser said it was a profound truth. 'People should do what they can do best,' he said, 'not go around embarrassing everybody by trying their hand at other people's specialities. Done properly, an extempore prayer is a rolling, magnificent thing, but it needs a Scotsman or a Methodist to handle it. Set an Anglican on and he will start off: "I have a photograph in my room O Lord ...".' Fraser said he had once heard some junior chaplain somewhere launch into a prayer with this very opening, and he still broke out in a muck sweat whenever the memory of it came back to him.

The door to the multi-storey was one of those infuriating efforts which only open from the inside, so we had to go round to the front of the carpark to get back in. This was a very new multi-storey, as multi-storeys go, and of course it was built with all the latest devices to prevent people finding their way back to their own cars. I used to think that they did this just to keep you parked for a bit longer so that you had to pay extra money, but I have come to realise that it's more than that. It's a matter of Civic Pride. Every now and then, as you know, the Mayor and Corporation of all aspiring boroughs let their hair down and relax – Tuesday afternoons, except bank-holidays, is the normal time for this sort of thing – and as they bask over their port and cigars they tick off on their fingers all their successes and triumphs since taking office to make sure they haven't missed any out. You know the style. 'Water-rate increase of 300 per cent in the last year, a row of alms-houses demolished to make way for a nice unwanted by-pass, curfew and compulsory identity cards imposed on all old-age pensioners. '*But*,' they say to themselves, '*But*. Let us not forget our greatest achievement. Market Postlethwaite – we say it with pride – Market Postlethwaite has now got the most incomprehensible multi-storey carpark in the whole of the South West.'

'Going to put in a multi-storey carpark, are you?' the City Architect says to the Borough Surveyor a month after the new administration has moved in. 'I wondered when you were going to get round to that. What sort of thing do you want?'

'I've got a budget of one million pounds,' the Borough Surveyor replies. 'More, if necessary. The Council wants the latest there is.'

'Good. Well, there are three basic designs, you know. There's the Coffin Lid, the Wormwood Scrubs and the Upturned Tank. They're all of them pretty ugly in their own way.'

'The ugliest will be good enough for us,' says the Borough Surveyor.

'Ah, then I recommend the Coffin Lid. It's a real monstrosity, and it has the added advantage of being very flexible when it comes to the extras. Now, let me see, you wanted the exterior staircases exposed to the prevailing wind, I take it? Okay. And how about malfunctioning lifts – shall we say two of those? You can either have the straightforward type which is permanently stopped between floors, or there's a new model out which makes a special whirring noise to deceive people into thinking it's on the move.'

Then they get down to the finer points: whether to number the floors from the top downward, staring with 4B at ground level and throwing in a mezzanine for good measure, or whether it's better to give no indication at all, so that people can wander round in an enormous corkscrew getting lost. They discuss the merits of putting up a series of notices saying *Way Out and Shopping Precinct* which ends up in a broom-cupboard on the roof; and they weigh the advantages of having Chinese language-students on the check-out barrier, as opposed to automatic machines which will only accept £2.70 in 10p pieces.

Henry and Fraser and I have an established multi-storey procedure perfected on previous excursions. We take one floor each, and after every search we come back to the barrier and start again. In this way somebody finds the car eventually, and provided he leaves a trail of torn newspaper we can all make our way back to it and get on the road.

Henry said, as we left Lichfield, that he found it a depressing place. He said that that was no particular reflection of Lichfield – he felt like that about all Cathedral cities. They gave him the willies, and he never seemed to go to one without some dismal experience or other happening to him.

Henry said that a year or so back he had once had to spend a night in Gloucester during the Three Choirs Festival and in a weak moment he bought a ticket to go to a concert in the evening. If it had been left to him he wouldn't have stayed in the town at all, but the firm he was helping out had booked him in there, so it seemed churlish to refuse. Besides, going to the concert, with perhaps a quick pint during the interval and a couple more when it was over, seemed such a harmless form of enjoyment that he couldn't believe that anything could go wrong.

He turned up at the concert just a few minutes before the performance started, and he positioned himself quite deliberately close to the door. When the interval came he was first out on to the pavement and started off across the square in search of a pub. He was just half-way across when it suddenly began to pelt with rain and he had to dash to the far side and take shelter in a covered arcade, in company with a dozen or more other pedestrians who had been caught in the squall. One of his fellow refugees was a small man of military appearance who seemed to be on much the same errand as himself. Whenever Henry looked at his watch and peered out into the rain, he noticed that his companion did the same. The man had a pleasantly mottled face, and after a while they agreed between themselves to take turns at the job so as not to duplicate effort.

The upshot of all this was, of course, that Henry and the military man became quite friendly. Between their dashes to the front of the arcade Henry explained to him the principle of Gunther's Theory of Averages, and the military man very decently gave him some tips on how to defend a hill-position against Burmese tribesmen in the monsoon season.

'It's beginning to ease off,' the military man said at last, returning from his latest sortie. 'What time do you make it?'

'It's just after nine,' said Henry. 'How long do you think we've got?'

'Oh, there's a good ten minutes yet,' said his friend. 'You're looking for The Paradise I take it?'

Henry said he was. He told us that he remembered thinking at the time what a marvellous name for a pub The Paradise was. So much more factual than your ordinary run-of-the-mill Red Lion or Lamb and Flag. He also thought how mulish and narrow he'd been all those years running down Cathedral cities in his own mind without a shred of justification, and he promised himself he would tell the military man all about it when they got to the bar, and ask him if he could recommend a penance.

'Right! Now, you stick close to me and I'll have you there in a jiffy,' said Henry's friend. 'It's a fairly narrow entry and you can miss it altogether if you don't know what you're doing.'

They set off at a cracking pace and within a hundred yards or so they dived right off the square and into a narrow doorway beside a betting-shop. Henry's tiny friend then sprang up a flight of stairs two at a time and threw the door open on to what seemed to be – and in fact was – a small committee room where five elderly ladies and three men were standing talking to each other. Henry still had the feeling at this stage that the room was some sort of drinking-club for the cognoscenti.

'By Gad, it's wet outside!' exclaimed the military man vigorously. 'We could do with something to warm us up. How about some coffee! Coffee all right for you?' he asked Henry, in the rather peremptory way of a man who was used to being obeyed.

Henry heard himself saying Yes, coffee was just what he was looking for.

It transpired in the next five minutes that what Henry had innocently let himself in for was a recital from memory of books one to six of *Paradise Lost* given by a bearded man whose collar wasn't frightfully clean. It took two and a quarter hours. During the whole of this time Henry sat listlessly by the window from where he could distinctly see the lights of a small and cheery tavern on the corner of a distant street. People seemed to go into it looking hopeful and come out looking contented.

As for the poem itself, Henry told us that he couldn't remember a single complete line of what he had heard. The only short phrase which stuck irremovably in his mind was when the bearded man at one point laid his larynx back to the ceiling and with all the dramatic impact of a wasp trying to hum through a comb in a paper bag, let rip with 'Hail, Holy Light!' At that moment the pub across the street was promptly plunged into darkness, taking with it Henry's last hope of getting a decent drink that evening.

The other members of the audience seemed to consider the 'Paradise' an enormous success, and they all stood around afterwards and laid daredevil plans to tackle books seven to twelve the following year. Henry was prepared by now to lie shamelessly in order to disentangle himself from the gathering, and he asked them to be sure to let him know the date so that he could hear what happened in the second half. In fact, as he splashed back to his hotel through the darkened streets, he took a solemn oath never to spend a night in a Cathedral city ever again. So Henry said he hoped Fraser and I hadn't got any funny ideas about stopping off in Shrewsbury.

Shrewsbury is not a Cathedral city, and I said so. Henry said he was sure I was right, but you could never be too careful and would we think it too silly of him if he asked us not to stay there just in case, and I said Not at all, that was the least we could do for a friend. And Fraser said he was hoping to press on well beyond Shrewsbury so that he we could get started promptly on the Dyke tomorrow. He said he didn't care for Shrewsbury in any case – and I said I didn't care for it either.

It's wonderful what a great bringer-together collective guilt is. I dare say if we had set off from Essex when we had meant to set off, and if we hadn't spent ten times as long as we expected in

Lichfield, we would have got to Shrewsbury by the early afternoon and have strolled round exclaiming at the wonders of the place. But now, to hear us talk, you would think that Shrewsbury had been deliberately put in our way to cause trouble. We said the town had been wrongly sited centuries ago and this accounted for its stunted growth. We tried to remember whether it had produced any famous sons, and we couldn't think of any and told each other we weren't in the least surprised; and then we turned to its public buildings, and we couldn't think of any of those either, except that Fraser said he thought the town gaol was supposed to be particularly fine, and Henry and I said that was logical.

Fraser got quite carried away after this and told us that he wanted to comment on the hotels, but Henry said No. He said that for over-pricing and bad service the town of B— had by far the worst hotels in the country and he was not prepared to hear his deepest convictions challenged by casual and uninformed abuse of anywhere else. If you stopped on the B— by-pass around dinner-time, Henry said, you could hear the grinding of tin-openers and the slitting of plastic bags from miles away as all the chefs in the town started preparing the evening meal. He said the sound was notorious, and doctors in the neighbourhood recommended it as a mild depressant to patients who were suffering from hyper-activity.

So we pressed on and went through Whittington and came to Gobowen. Fortune was with us, because the chances of one person let alone three finding a bed in a town like Gobowen at eight o'clock at night must be extremely thin. Fraser said the odds must be a thousand to one, but Henry said they weren't as great as that. He couldn't think what they actually were at the moment, but he would work it out later on while he was having a beer.

The place we stayed at was a boarding-house called The Balmoral. It had a nice welcoming sign outside which said 'Vacancies', and inside it was all brightness and flocked wallpaper. We washed and changed and strolled round to the Hart and Trumpet for a chicken in the basket and a pint of Border Ale.

Henry went quite quiet after his first pint and a half, and he settled down to calculate the odds on finding a room. Five minutes later Fraser and I realised that this was just an excuse for him to go to sleep. So we woke the fraud up and steered him across the road to The Balmoral and laid him out on his bed and took off his shoes.

'I'll get into bed in a minute,' he told us as we shut the door.

And a minute later there were loud snores coming from Henry's room, which, as I explained to Fraser, demonstrated beyond doubt that he either had got into bed or he hadn't.

# 5

# Stepping it Out

When Fraser and I got down to breakfast next morning we found Henry surrounded by maps. Other people who were having breakfast at the same time seemed to take it in good part, saying politely that they didn't want to disturb him but if he looked under the two or three sheets nearest the window they thought he might find a jar of marmalade. One of them even suggested giving the salt-pot a grid reference so that they could all relocate it without disturbing him.

This of course was Henry laying down an elaborate ground-bait as an excuse for not doing any serious walking. Henry's philosophy is that if you arm yourself with enough in the way of equipment and charts you can pass the day pleasantly enough browsing over it all without rising from a sitting position. Old hands like Henry can actually start panting and perspiring just at the sight of a hill on a map which they pretend to themselves they are going to be walking up around the middle of the day.

He should have known it wouldn't wash with us. Fraser and I merely put him in charge of map-reading for the whole of the holiday and went outside to deal with the car and the luggage.

I don't know how many years it is since I last looked at a map, but in principle I refuse to do it. Among the male sex I am unique in this respect. Women have much more sense.

I remember going for a walk one day with two men and their wives in the highlands of Scotland. There were children involved as well, which only made it worse. The men said we were going to strike up Ben Boggart by the back route, take a look at the view and then toddle down again. I asked them whether we ought to take any equipment, and they smiled indulgently at each other over their toast and told me not to worry my head about that sort of thing. They said we'd only be gone a couple of hours, and they thrust a map under my nose and told me to take a look for myself. Then they called the waiter over – we were staying in a shooting-hotel – and asked him to tell the manager that we would be wanting venison for lunch.

I went up to my room and stuffed my pockets full of chocolate and tied up four blankets with a dressing-gown cord. I told them it would make it more comfortable if we decided to sit down for a rest.

We all started off in grand style. We strode down the drive of the hotel, with the children skipping along in front, and we came to the road. We walked along it for a little way and then turned off through a gate, which the two men said was clearly marked on the map. About a mile further on, the track we were walking along faded out in the heather, but my friends said it didn't matter because they had been planning to cut the corner off anyway, and we could join the unmetalled mountain road further down.

We walked on for about half an hour when suddenly one of the wives stopped and asked her husband which of the hills Ben Boggart actually was.

'It's that one over there, sweetheart,' he replied encouragingly, selecting a peak from the thirty or more within view. 'We're a good half-way to it by now.'

She asked him whether he was sure it was that one, because it didn't look the same shape as the one we'd seen from the hotel.

He said he was absolutely sure, and then the other man came and looked at the map for some time and said he felt pretty certain that that was probably the one as well. He said the outline of the summit changed when you approached it from an unfamiliar angle, and the fact that it looked so different now was a sure sign of the progress we had made.

About half a mile further on my two friends fell into a squabble about which peak they had both agreed they were aiming for ten minutes before.

'That's it there,' one would say, pointing dramatically towards the left.

'Oh don't be a fool,' the other would tell him. 'It's this one on the right. Can't you read a map? Look, we are here ...'

'Here?' the first one would exclaim, scornfully dabbing his finger at the page. 'We're not here! We're over *here*!'

Then the other wife suggested that wherever we were we should all turn and go back. And they both rounded on her and told her not to be idiotic. They said that if they couldn't take their families for a short stroll without them throwing in the towel after the first couple of fields things had come to a pretty pass.

The wife replied with some spirit that she was afraid we might all get lost and die of exposure without ever being found again, and they told her that was quite impossible and she shouldn't make jokes about things she didn't understand.

Then, about twenty minutes later, we came across the carcass of a sheep, which set the children crying, and after that they all had to be carried on our shoulders.

At noon I shared out half my chocolate. We ate it beside a small loch which seemed not to be on the map at all. At tea-time we huddled into a gulley in the side of a hill and had half of what was left. Nobody had any idea where we were, but the more they got us lost the more enthusiastic my two friends became about their ability to map-read us out. At last, at about six o'clock – and without a word of advance warning from our guides – we stumbled over the top of a gentle rise in the heather and found ourselves standing on a wide tarmacked road. As a party we were pretty well dead-beat, but the appearance of this sudden aid to navigation seemed rather to annoy my friends than the reverse. Although the two of them had wildly conflicting opinions as to where we were actually standing, they both agreed that the road had no business being there in the first place. They seemed to look upon it as a sort of mirage, and they said the important thing was to establish which way north was so that we could strike out from the road at the correct angle. They said this could easily be done by putting a stick in the ground and observing which way the shadow of the sun was pointing at midday, but the wives said they weren't prepared to wait.

Five minutes later a lorry came round the corner and I waved it down and asked the driver if he would take us back to the hotel. He said he didn't have enough petrol for that length of journey, but if we cared to jump in he could run us into Inverness which was just a couple of miles away and then we could hire a taxi from there.

So I'm always happy to be guided by someone else when it comes to map-reading. It's not that I have any particular faith in their skill at finding the way, but at least it means that I don't get any of the blame when we go wrong.

Fraser and I got the back-packs assembled, and we threw all the luggage which we had thought we were going to need but didn't back into the car. There's nothing like a real-life situation for making you practical. Everyone can have theories about how a back-pack goes together. Everyone can sit round at home and draw up lists of what is essential and what isn't; but lay it all down at the feet of the man who is just setting off, and he will sort out what's to be carried and how before you can say knife.

We parked the car at Gobowen station and I phoned home to Widget to tell her where it was. As we came out of the station a man appeared from the ticket office and told us we couldn't leave the car there. He said it was against the by-laws, and it was reserved for the district manager, and the parking charge would be two pounds seventy-five a day. I was all for telling him to belt up and clear off, but Fraser said I didn't understand the psychology of the man. He wasn't basically obstreperous, he said, just bored to tears from having nothing to do, and his appalling lack of courtesy was in reality a cry for help. So we asked him to quote us for two adults and five children travelling from Gobowen to Prague via Weymouth on a family railcard during the off-peak season and said we would return for the information the next day. The last we saw of him he was surrounded by four time-tables busily telephoning Paddington and looking the picture of contentment.

Fraser dashed into a chemist's shop and bought a razor – notice how long that non-shaving resolution of his lasted. Then we loaded Henry up into his pack, and after a short dispute as to which bundle was the heavier we set off walking along the road to Selattyn. You have to take a strong line with Henry when it comes to demarcation disputes.

Our plan was – and we kept to it well – to avoid as far as possible anything that resembled a main road. By-roads are fine when you're hiking. Busy roads are a nightmare. To hop from the hard surface on to the verge whenever a car comes round the corner is an easy enough thing for a jogger in a tracksuit, but for a man in a full pack and boots a steady uninterrupted roll of forward movement is essential. So, instead of turning north to Selattyn when we struck the Oswestry road, we crossed it leaving the little town on our right and made on up the narrowing lanes towards Pant-glas and Caregy-big.

The sun shone brightly but not too hot, and from the west a refreshing wind was sending tufts of torn cloud across his face, their shadows sweeping the hillsides like squadrons of horse. Ahead and far across the border the dark peak of Cadair Bronwen, the seat of Arthur, towered prophetically above its greener slopes.

It is a strange thing about Wales, but it is one of those countries which seems to overspill its boundaries along the whole length of its border. It does it in every way it can – in the landscape, in the place names, in the accents and attitudes of the people – so that several miles before you actually come to the dividing line you have the sensation of being in Wales already. Now suppose you were to move the border five miles east. You would probably swing the balance the other way and everybody would remark how English all the altered counties seemed to be and they would set up a boundary commission which would worry over the problem for years and years and eventually move the line back to where it was in the first place. Some frontiers just seem to behave themselves naturally, and others never quite will: the Mediterranean boundary between France and Italy has not – so far as I know – caused anyone any problems for years. On one side they smoke Gauloises and on the other side they eat spaghetti, and each inhabitant seems to be quite clear about which of the two he is supposed to be doing. But run a little way north up into Alsace, and there you have a population which has actually taught itself to speak two languages – one for present use, and the other to have up its sleeve for the next time somebody moves the frontier about.

I shared these thoughts of mine with Fraser. He said that most of the problems over frontiers arose because the people who fixed the boundaries started from false premises. He said the ordinary man wasn't interested in high-blown cultural distinctions. What he *was* interested in was which town he was going to drive to on market day to get himself a roll of chicken-wire, and so long as the line traced its way accurately between the catchment areas of the various border towns a frontier could work perfectly well for centuries.

Henry didn't contribute to this conversation. It was probably too philanthropic for him. Henry is quite as capable as the next man of having his own flights of fancy – poetry, abstract theory, call it what you will – but his muse does really like something personal to get its teeth into.

A purple passage of Henry's *Reflections* will go something like this:

> So here we are walking along a road towards the Welsh border. My feet are warm and that is quite satisfactory. Ahead of me there is a large mountain, but since we are not planning to climb it I don't particularly mind. In point of fact its outline reminds me of a cheese sandwich. Ah, cheese, cheese, how manifold are the blessings you have conferred upon a grateful mankind! Were I to list the various forms and flavours that you assume, how many volumes might I not fill! So I will confine myself to mentioning toasted cheese grilled till it's brown on top and rounded off with a pinch of red pepper or tabasco. Incidentally I don't think we ought to delay lunch too long today. It's all very well saying we'll stop somewhere five miles on and that should take us an hour and a half, but what's the land like in between? Now if Offa had really wanted to make a name for himself, he could have designed the dyke so that it ran downhill all the way and had leisure centres and amenity areas dotted along it at three-mile intervals. I hope it doesn't rain ...

And so on. That is the stream of consciousness as far as Henry is concerned. If Henry had lived in the eighteenth century and had gone on the Grand Tour he would have been the only one who didn't fall back gasping with romantic wonderment at the sight of Mont Blanc. He would merely have shuffled uneasily from foot to foot and asked the guide if they had to go over the top or whether there was a quick way round the side.

On the far edge of Pant-glas we met a man standing beside a shooting-brake. We asked him if we were near to Offa's Dyke, and he said No. This cheered us up no end. I should explain that this wasn't a helpful prefatory sort of No, the sort of No you may give to a foreign tourist who has found his way into the post office and has to be set back on course for the railway station. The No that we got was the all-encompassing black-as-night variety. The type of No that grips the heart of the inexperienced hiker in a manacle of despair and sends him back home again to Potter's Bar wondering how he could ever have been so weak-minded as to believe that the place he was walking to ever existed at all. Then he wanders listlessly around the house making himself scrambled eggs and trying to play games of pelmanism with himself to see how far his mind has deteriorated. And the following week he gives his boots and knapsack away to Oxfam and buys himself a book on growing indoor geraniums.

Of course the experienced hiker knows these massive doom-laden No's of old, and he doesn't flinch from them one bit. In fact after the first five or six that he runs up against in his lifetime – more or less the point that Henry and Fraser and I have got to by now – he actually begins to enjoy them and takes them as a welcome sign that he is getting near his destination.

There are naturally several forms of the doom-laden No. There is the Rustic Stupidity variety: 'Oi've lived here man and boy for getting on seventy year or darned near, and dang me if oi've ever heerd of any house or mansion or such round these parts. No, oi'm darned if oi 'ave.' This type is generally delivered in, say, the churchyard at Woodstock with the heroic silhouette of Blenheim Palace framed as a backdrop. Then there's the man who knows that what you're looking for isn't there, because he's walking in the opposite direction and he hasn't passed anything more interesting than a silo.

But of all these No's by far the most devastating are those delivered by the landowner of affluence and education whose roots lie deep in the soil you are standing on – in a word, by the Squire. What *he* says really *must* be right.

'Battlefield? *Battle*field?' one such man exclaimed to me a few years ago as we stood on the point outside the village of Naseby, whence Cromwell had launched the charge that changed the entire course of English history. 'No. N … no. Nothing like that round here. You wouldn't be thinking of Stonehenge by any chance?'

So it was with our man in the shooting-brake – a good example of the genre. Were we getting close to Offa's Dyke? No. Did the Dyke run along this part of the country at all? No – not so far as he was aware. Did he have any idea where we might hope to bump into it? He couldn't say. He gave the impression that anyone who wanted to try their hand at dyke-making in his neighbourhood would have to ask him about it first.

We thanked him courteously and moved on.

We found the Dyke about half a mile up the road. You can't mistake it. It's about thirty feet deep with giant banks of green turf on both sides of it. It is about as unobtrusive as a tidal wave.

With the pre-planned efficiency of true professionals we spun a coin to decide whether to turn left or right and eventually set off southwards. We walked along the floor of the Dyke in an unsteady line. I led the way, chiefly to prevent Fraser from setting too wild a pace. Fraser brought up the rear to make sure that Henry didn't sit down and fall asleep over his maps. That's how we work, Fraser and Henry and I – as a team.

I suppose it was just because it was our first day out but we really found ourselves in the mood for walking. By the time we actually reached the Dyke it was eleven o'clock in the morning, an hour which normally catches us in a reflective frame of mind and looking for a quiet spot to chew over the day's progress so far. But today we were all zest and spring – and we stuck to it.

We hadn't been out for five minutes before the message came up the line from Fraser telling me to stop dawdling and step it out, and Henry said he endorsed the opinion with brass knobs on. Then I said to Fraser that it seemed a pity to stop for lunch – just when we were getting on so well, as it were – and Fraser agreed. He said sandwiches and pints in pubs were the walker's prize for a job well done, and by definition you couldn't win a prize when you were only half-way through the race. Henry said he thought we ought to give it a try to see whether you could or not, but we told him he would be left behind if he did, and this seemed to steady his nerve and keep him going.

So we strode along right through the middle of the day without so much as a pause.

You, Gentle Reader, will want to know from me what the countryside was like.

Well, we went up over a hill and round the edge of another and past a sort of thingummy in the side of the bank which was made of stone and looked like an Anglo-Saxon bus-shelter, which of course it can't be. Then we went down a very steep bit and over a river and up the other side where it was all covered with ivy, and we had to pull ourselves up by tugging at the tufts of it growing out of the slope. Then we found ourselves suddenly skirting the edge of a golf-course, and Fraser said that that reminded him of a joke. And Henry said if it was his one about the Ladies' Champion and the No.4 iron could he please start with the punchline and work backwards so we could all get our laughs in while we were still fresh. And Fraser said it *wasn't* that joke, but if that was the way Henry felt about it he wouldn't tell a joke at all. And Henry said he bet it *was* that joke really, and Fraser was obviously refusing to tell another because he didn't know any more.

Then we walked through a village at about tea-time and alongside a road and past a disused railway station and back into some fields again, where we found the Dyke very decently waiting for us – because we seemed to have lost it for the past ten minutes or so.

Now you may say that this is a very unromantic description of Offa's Dyke, and so it is. But consider what Fraser and I had to put up with as we went along, and you will see why I prefer to tell it that way. Unbeknown to us, Henry, our official map-reader, also seemed to have appointed himself as unofficial Guardian of the Guidebooks. This sort of thing has happened before, so we can't exactly say we didn't know about it – the trouble is that you don't notice these attacks coming on until they've really got a grip on a man.

You've probably experienced the agony of the ever-present guidebook carrier. Properly and sparingly used – and used in the right place – a guidebook is exactly what we need to keep us informed: 'We now enter the main quadrangle of Baldwyn College, Oxford. The stone gateway with its elaborate fluted niches bears the arms of the founder, Egwyte, Bishop of Winchester (1021). Visitors should notice the finely carved statue of Walpole which occupies the left-hand recess and try to ignore the present-day Provost who has propped himself up on the right to sleep it off.' This sort of thing is helpful.

What is not helpful is when you are rushing across the

platform at Euston for a train which is just pulling out and your companion with the guidebook draws you aside to point out that the domed roof is the work of Arnold Crump the Younger (1864-1927) and that the stained-glass portrait of a dachshund over the clock is generally considered to be his finest achievement.

Nor, to come back to our case, when your feet have slipped and you are hanging on to a hillside for dear life – something which happened to me briefly on those ivy-clad slopes – are you best pleased to be touched on the arm by your nearest and dearest and informed in a confidential whisper that Offa's Dyke never fails to command the view to the westward. One can see *that* for oneself: it just seems a pity that Offa didn't put a little more landscape between the view and the man who is about to fall into it.

Yes, we had trouble with Henry. Not a corner did we round, not a hill did we breast, but Henry was one jump ahead of us with some prepared comment or other. If these guidebooks would only confine themselves to straightforward major facts they might be just bearable: *The 120 foot Dorian column which dominates the western skyline was erected by the Duchess of Beaufort in 1743 in memory of her favourite spaniel, Ruffles*. But no. Minor facts – the silliest minor facts you ever met – are studded through the whole concoction like currants. 'By now you are walking on gravel,' the book may say fatuously, or 'You enter the Huntsman's Arms by the front door' – as though you had to be restrained from sliding down the chimney and jumping out of the fireplace in the saloon bar and saying 'Boo'.

And as for the opinions – you know, 'Probably the finest panorama in south-west Montgomeryshire', or 'What richer enjoyment can there be than to stretch out amid the luxuriant pastures of this enamoured vale and gaze upon the laughing springs of the Llemonaydd as, dashing out between the rocks of Vyrnwy, it hurtles, turbulent, towards its confluence with the majestic Severn.' Not a word about the fact that the alleged stream is bone dry for four months in the summer. No mention of the mosquitoes. Dead silence on the cow-pats which litter the bank like mushrooms in a grow-bag. Huh.

That evening, when Henry wasn't looking, Fraser and I collected together every map and guide and leaflet that we could find and we gave them to the landlord of the Llanbader Arms. And we gave him a five-pound note as well. And we asked him to put them in a parcel and post them off back home.

But I'm running ahead ...

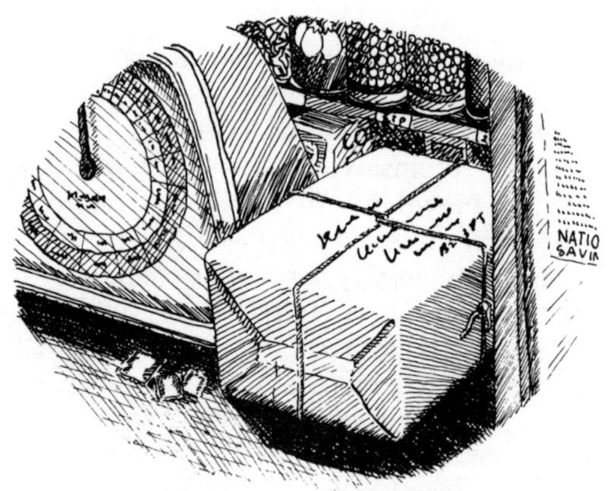

# 6

# Knocking it Back

We camped for the night in the bottom of the Dyke. In the last mile or so before we stopped Offa seemed to have taken it into his head to shallow his earthwork out – perhaps the labour force wouldn't agree to the overtime – and as we walked off across the fields in search of civilisation we could look back and see the orange top-ridge of our little tent from more than a mile away.

The sleeping-under-canvas decision was mine, and I very sensibly forced it on the others. Henry was for finding an inn that would put us up, but I told him it wasn't practical. The whole idea of an inn, a Welsh or English inn, is a largely mythical notion foisted on to overseas visitors and weak-minded natives by the various Tourist Authorities. The very vagueness of the word ought to put us on our guard against it.

Britain offers two basic institutions to the traveller. One is the hotel, a place of computerised bills and unforeseen surcharges rightly avoided by every plain man in command of his faculties. The other is the pub, small, welcoming, much loved, and offering no accommodation. That 'inns' do actually exist, in the sense of pubs which have bedrooms for visitors as well, I won't try to deny. But to wander out into an unfamiliar countryside and expect to find one when you need it would be an act of pure folly. They just don't occur that often.

So it seemed to me that the putting up of a tent and the laying down of sleeping-bags would solve the accommodation side of the equation, and the finding of a pub would solve the eating and washing side – and, of course, the question of thirst.

I was looking forward to a Welsh pub. I said we might be able to join in some singing. Fraser said he would advise against it. He was second to none, he said, in his respect for my vocal range, and at breaking wine-glasses round the dinner table he would back my delivery against all comers; but musical people when they heard me might become unpredictable and violent. It was their artistic temperament.

Fraser said that because of our long-standing friendship and the deep affection and esteem in which we held each other, he knew I would take it in the right spirit when he said that my singing voice was one of the lousiest, loudest, flattest, most cacophonous imitations of gas escaping from a snapped-off mains that he'd ever heard. It was almost as bad, he said, as his friend B's. In fact, he said, it would be interesting to put B and me in for a music competition just to see who came out bottom.

The tragedy about B, Fraser said, was that if people had only been frank to him about his voice in the first place he wouldn't have got ideas above his station. Properly trained he might have made an excellent auctioneer or bookmaker. It all began apparently when he was idly flicking through the *Standard* one evening on his way back from work and he came across one of those dense closely-worded advertisements which are actually headed *Advertisement* across the top and then go on to tell you that there is an amazing new method that will enable you to get to grips with colloquial Icelandic, or the Oxford English Dictionary, or the oboe, in ten weeks starting next Saturday.

This particular advertisement was about singing. According to B, it asked all sorts of enticing questions about whether you could spare two hours a day to master Handel's *Messiah* and sing the tenor solos at the beginning of next month. There was a letter from 'Mr D.S. of Huddersfield (address supplied)' explaining how this course had transformed his life, opening up new vistas of artistic appreciation and achievement which he had never before thought possible. Mr D.S. stated quite baldly that the time spent on the singing course would be 'probably the most self-revealing three weeks you will ever spend in your life.'

It was the fact that this was only a three-week course that ultimately decided B in favour of trying it. Up to that time he had been wavering between two other courses, one on making candlewick bedspreads and the other on laying concrete; but as they both required ten weeks of study he thought he'd try his hand at something easier.

He wrote away for the course, and eventually it arrived. He did his first day's practice and then came downstairs and sang his mother two verses of 'On Top of Old Smokey' and asked her to guess what it was. She said she thought it must be something to do with sheep-dog trials, but B wasn't in the least put off. He told Fraser that his instruction manual had warned him not to be surprised if dull unmusical people were slow to respond to the progress he was making in the early stages.

B didn't see much of his family in the course of the next three weeks. He normally did his practice in the mornings, and he noticed that most of the household would slip away on a variety of errands soon after breakfast and come back warily just before lunch so as not to disturb him. In the afternoons, when B would occasionally run over his daily lesson a second time just to make sure he had it licked, his mother suggested he might like to make use of the summer-house at the end of the garden, but his father said No – he didn't want to lose the gardener. He said he was prepared to hire B a lock-up garage or an aircraft hanger, provided they weren't near a centre of population.

Yet for all their sarcasm and evasiveness B's family still stopped short of the sort of downright abuse which was what the situation really required. B was so enthusiastic about his own progress that he managed to interpret anything less than foul language or a blood-curdling oath as an actual compliment.

By the time his three weeks were up, B felt he had the subject of music mastered. He rang up the correspondence school and told them so, and the Principal said that this was quite usual but they could accept no liability for the consequences.

That afternoon B's mother had two of her aunts coming to tea and B laid out one of his most advanced pieces rather ostentatiously on the piano to catch their attention. While his mother was in the kitchen setting the tea-tray, B nudged the sheet of music off the piano so that it floated down under the aunts' noses, and Aunt Hermione picked it up and said that she would play the accompaniment if B agreed to sing it for them. B said he would. He said he didn't normally give private performances at short notice, but as the ladies were so appreciative of good music he would make an exception in this case.

B's piece was a sombre and passionate work. Fraser said it was called 'The Two Grenadiers' and was by Schumann, neither of which bits of information means very much to me. It seems that to give the song its full impact it has to be sung in German, but that was no problem for B because the pronunciation of foreign languages had been fully covered in Lesson Five of the course. B said that the first few notes were for the piano only, a dark rumbling of foreboding, and then the voice entered alone with a melody of such ethereal drama that at the original performance many of the audience were weeping silently by the end of the first line.

This wasn't quite the effect that B produced on the two aunts. When his moment came to sing, B filled his lungs and gave it all he'd got:

*Nach Frankreich zogen zwei Grenadier*

The noise that B made was so dramatic and unearthly that by way of reaction he received a moan like a failing gannet from the listening aunt, while Aunt Hermione started back from the keyboard and struck the wall behind her with her head. B maintained afterwards that it was the shock waves from this impact which brought down the engraving of 'When Did You Last See Your Father', not his singing. The shock waves from *that* (B said) had died away a full dotted minim of musical time before.

B's mother heard the impact and came into the room to give assistance. To outward appearance the two aunts were none the worse for their experience. But their emotions were badly bruised, and no amount of cucumber sandwiches seemed to be able to effect a cure. They left early and went home muttering darkly about altering their wills, but fortunately they were too shaken to remember.

If B had only been told the truth by his family in the first place (Fraser said) this painful episode need never have occurred.

Fraser finished his account just as we swung on to the hard road that leads to the Llanbeder Arms, and by the time we had got inside the door he and Henry had made me promise not to get involved in any sing-songs on my own behalf. They said I could leave the singing work to them, but I might make my own contribution by beating time silently with a beer-mat. I agreed to do this. Not, you understand, because I am not capable of making up my own mind about singing – contrary to what Fraser was saying I sing a very passable light tenor. I agreed because I am a man of peace, and I am always prepared to refrain from argument in order to please a friend.

I don't harbour grudges. That isn't my way at all. But I must say, in view of Fraser's wounding criticisms on the way to the pub, it was uplifting to see a certain justice at work in the way he made a complete fool of himself once he was in it. Music, fortunately, had nothing to do with the matter.

Fraser, you see, thinks he has a knack of getting on with the locals when he arrives in an unfamiliar pub. Actually, the only knack he has is for embarrassing everybody else in the room except himself.

As you know, it's a proven fact that the locals in a country pub are impossible to get to know – at least for the first two dozen visits or so. These are the silent, sand-blasted men whose chief emotions on seeing you are disbelief and resentment. For a stranger to take the sign 'public bar' in the literal sense, meaning that he is allowed to walk into the place, seems to them to be playing with words, not to say exploiting a legal loophole – and they don't like smart alecs.

Because of this feeling of being an intruder, most people of sensitivity and breeding have adopted a code of conduct which goes broadly as follows:

1. Use the saloon bar, not the public bar.
2. Address no stranger other than the landlord.
3. Keep eyes lowered to carpet throughout visit, and, if talking among yourselves, do so in embarrassed, intermittent whispers.
4. On departure slink out furtively with inaudible muttered 'Goodbye', putting your glass back on the bar as you go.

That is the way the gentleman behaves.

With Fraser it is different. To start with, so long as he is in England he will address his remarks to everybody in a manure-heavy Mummerset accent which brings all his friends out in a prickly rash. He doesn't vary the dialect, either. I suppose, since it resembles nothing in heaven or on earth, it can't matter very much that the same travesty of a rustic burr is used indiscriminately to, say, a Derbyshire shepherd, a Wiltshire farmer, or a Lincolnshire poacher, but one does expect people to be called by their proper names. It can't help, one would think, to have random Christian names such as Bill, Alf and Fred simply allocated for the evening among the inhabitants at the whim of a man who has just that minute stepped into the bar.

Fraser normally starts by hailing the landlord. 'Woy, zone me, Ned, if it baint a roight zedzy old noight out zere. Woy oi be zo barky oi could fanzy a drop of zat zere zbecial brew you bid oidin out ze back zere, for me and moi matez these lazt zix weeks an more, heh heh!'

Whereupon the landlord looks surprised and remarks that the chemist is closed at this time of night but he does have a bottle of syrup-of-figs upstairs if he thinks it will ease the pain.

On this occasion Fraser spoke Welsh, and it really was a show-stopper. We found out afterwards that the words meant something about peeling onions, but I suppose the fact that he'd got six words – any words – of Gaelic off by heart was a sufficient gesture in the direction of local colour from Fraser's point of view.

Henry and I took our beer and cowered into a corner to watch, as Fraser sauntered expansively into the middle of the room. About sixteen other pairs of eyes were watching as well. Fraser selected a man in a cap who had been playing table skittles and – cursorily re-baptising him 'Daffy' – offered to buy him a drink. Without dropping his stare the man drained the beer down his throat and handed over his glass. Three other empty glasses appeared at the same time, and in the mugs around the walls there was a general lowering of beer levels. The feeling was beginning to spread around the Llanbeder Arms that they could be on to something.

When Fraser returned with the beer the man in the cap and two of his cronies converged and offered to play him a game of skittles. They let him win twice – that was before they started to bet on the result. After that, until Henry and I were able to prize him away from the pub at 11.15, he played nine games of skittles and lost every one. Sometimes they played him at singles, sometimes they would ask him to play doubles. Sometimes they would cruise comfortably to victory by a wide margin, and at other times they would let him get ahead and then creep up and overtake him at the last moment. And all this time Fraser actually imagined that he was making friends with them – making friends and improving his skittle-playing technique. 'Give me another couple of games,' he seemed to be saying unrepentantly to himself as we frog-marched him out into the yard. 'Give me another couple of games and I'll have got the technique sorted out.' And, do you know, I actually think he believed himself.

We were followed away from the pub by a small black-and-white dog. It was a terrier type with a black patch over one eye and a tail which curled upwards like a boomerang. It trotted in and out of our legs tripping us up and gazing ahead in an intrepid-explorer sort of way, trying to give the impression that it had been with us for weeks. 'Hello again, you lot,' it told us, swerving nimbly away from a kick which I aimed in its direction. 'It's me. I'm back. Just had to break off for a couple of days to climb one of the local peaks but I'm back with you now. Been managing all right without me, have you? Oh good. Well, let's get on with it then. No point in hanging around talking.'

We took the animal aside and gave it a piece of our mind. We told it we didn't know it from Adam, and although we had been prepared to go along with its Walter Mitty fantasies for a hundred yards or so the joke had gone far enough. We said that real-life explorers like ourselves had been known to eat dogs when the going got rough, and the best thing it could do was go back home and dig up a bone and try to forget.

The message seemed to have some effect. From weaving around our feet like a bobbin, the dog first of all fell in line behind us, and then eventually stopped altogether. The last we saw of it as we turned off the road into the fields it was sitting down under the end lamp-post in the village staring after us. 'And a fat lot of co-operation I got from *you*!' was clearly written across its face.

I'm not normally in the habit of dreaming, but this particular walk seemed to bring on a year's supply of dreams within the space of a few days. On the day we set out, if you remember, I had that dream about somebody shearing a sheep which actually turned out to be Katrina on the telephone. I can't remember what I dreamed the next night – presumably something so terrifying that the good old subconscious got out its blue pencil and censored it. Then this night I had the very vivid idea that I was sleeping with a suitcase on my chest. It wasn't just a straightforward leather or moulded suitcase either, it was a soft moleskin job which somebody had sensibly filled with small clockwork trains which were puffing in unison. What with the heat inside the tent and the weight of the suitcase on my chest, I was puffing quite a bit too; but whenever I tried to open the lid to tell the trains to synchronise their puffing with mine, the handle of the suitcase would uncurl itself and lick my nose.

All this seemed perfectly correct and sensible, of course – you know how it does. But it was when all the trains suddenly stopped puffing for a moment and instead the suitcase filled up with air and heaved an enormous sigh of boredom that the chain of rational events suddenly seemed to break and I opened my eyes to find a black-and-white dog of the terrier class fast asleep on my torso.

I say 'fast asleep', but actually it was more lying doggo, if that isn't a pun. It had its limbs spread out in an attitude of repose – tail down, chin firmly tucked in between the front paws – but its eyes, when you looked at them, were watching me closely for the first signs of life. In fact our friend of the night before had now thrown off his intrepid-explorer rôle and was playing a new game of being the psychoanalyst who is bringing the patient out of his coma. 'You have been in a deep, deep sleep,' he was saying in his best bedside manner. 'You have been in a deep, deep sleep, but now you are beginning to throw off your trance. Gently, gently, wakey wakey. Now, I am going to sniff three times and then I want you to open your eyes. Ready. Sniff ... sniff ... *sniff*. There we are!' And then, of course, being only a dog and not a fully-trained psychoanalyst at all, he couldn't disguise his amazement when I did actually open my eyes, and he leaped up on to all four paws, as though he had just seen a rat that needed jumping on, and began lathering my face with his tongue by way of saying, 'Yippee I've done it.'

I threw the dog to one side with my elbow and it landed on the motionless form of Henry. Henry sat up abruptly and said 'Whawazzatter?', and the sudden movement of his body jerked it on to Fraser. Fraser, snoring loudly and without opening his eyes, somehow managed to pick the animal up quite deftly in both hands and sent it hurtling back across the tent to me. He judged the throw nicely in the circumstances, so that the dog faded away from my outstretched left arm and bounced off the tent walls back on to Henry's face as he was sitting scratching his head and wondering what had hit him the first time.

By now the dog was bounding around our little bivouac in a series of rapid circles, and considering all the abuse and the footwear that were being thrown at him he seemed to be settling into the task of wrecking the homestead very well. Probably it was just the effect he had been hoping to achieve. One moment all had been peace and tedium, the next the world had emptied into a snowstorm of bloodcurdling oaths and misdirected punches and hiking boots. It was the sort of thing, he was telling himself, that you might have planned for months and months, and then never got within miles of it for sheer spontaneous confusion. Then, just as I had got him cornered by the door and was on the point of smothering him for good and all with a sleeping-bag, he wriggled backwards under the tent flap, ran off to a distance of fifty yards or so and lay down on his tummy to bark. He reappeared at breakfast – by which time we were all too exhausted and depressed to take the matter up with him – and joined the circle for a bowl of instant porridge and a slice of corned beef.

Wherever we went for the rest of that week, this dog went with us. I don't mean by that that he was one of the party. Not in a regular sense. He had far too much on his agenda to spend his time strolling along the fields and lanes with the likes of us – relations to visit, insurrections and guerilla movements to get under way, action committees of the MCM (Maverick Canine Movement) to address. Sometimes we wouldn't see him for whole days together; and then, just when we were beginning to forget about him completely, he would pop out at us from along the line of a hedgerow and fall in step for twenty minutes or so. 'So here you are,' he would say. 'I wondered when you'd be catching up. Not getting along too fast, are we, but then I suppose we can't expect too much from an inferior species. Well, it's been nice talking to you. I'd like to stay longer, but you know how it is – duty calls. Look, I'll see if I can't get back to you later in the evening. Either that or tomorrow morning. Sorry I can't be more precise. I say – is that the time? Cheerio – must dash.' And off he would go.

It was a foggy morning, with visibility down to about ten yards or so, and after breakfast Fraser and Che Woofera the dog disappeared into the mist and could be heard talking together. Henry and I thought it was one of those serious man-to-man conversations. Actually it was nothing of the kind, it was Fraser trying to shave with his new razor and the dog taking an active interest in seeing how the job was done. Together the two of them managed to produce a result like a porcupine in the moulting season.

There was a time, was there not, when the good old-fashioned razor-blade – I mean the standard Gillette or Pal razor-blade – was common bartering material throughout the known world. Some countries actually used them as coinage. Twelve oranges equal one razor-blade. Forty razor-blades equal one second-hand bicycle, and so on. Then somebody invented the electric razor, and the whole monetary system of the Third World was thrown into confusion. Panicking under the threat to the scratch-and-soap method of shaving, all the traditional razor-blade makers fell over themselves to invent their own new variation on the ageless theme of chomping the stubble from your chin. Single-sided blades, self-sharpening blades, built-in throwaway blades, double-headed swivel-topped blades, and so on and so on. The result, chaos. I am told that in the emerging world today you can't pass on a razor-blade for love nor money. Worse than that you can't *buy* the blade you need to fit the razor you got yourself in Worcester Park before you set out.

'Shopkeeper, tell me, do you have stock of the K139 super-swivel razor blade?'

'Yallaballala bingi-bingi. Thirty thousand Gillette bladies 1932 model. Very cheap.'

'That is no use to me. It must be the K139 or nothing.'

'Wama mama Q387 Extra Whizzer de luxe?'

'No. K139.'

'Skrapeorama D14, biddudda dudda?'

'No, I tell you. No.'

'Pikko pikko. Bakko bakko. Um Mburole on krumplawa bonga ki nwaloginda zutozumo powela um awapo.'

'What a ridiculous suggestion.'

'Bottla whisky?'

'Of course not. I can't shave with a bottle of whisky!'

'Perhaps not,' says the shopkeeper, suddenly remembering his days at Oxford, 'but it induces very desirable oblivion.'

The economic consequence is stagnation.

Fraser's razor – (how's that for an advertising catchphrase!) – Fraser's razor I think *was* the K139. He can't be sure about it because he had to tear the instructions off the back of the packet to get to the two free razor heads, and the dog swallowed them. I mean to say, he swallowed the instructions not the razor heads. Later in the proceedings he did in fact swallow one of the razor heads too, but he didn't seem to enjoy it much and left the other one for shaving with, so that if only Fraser had had the instructions he ought to have been all right. As it was, all he could remember was a picture of a man looking glumly into the mirror with a shadow round his chin you could cut with a lawn-mower. Then the 'after' cartoon showed him gleaming unpleasantly and reflecting the sunrise like a chandelier. Exactly how he had fitted the head on to the razor to achieve this result, Fraser couldn't for the life of him remember.

All this of course was lost on Henry and me. We could only hear the voices:

> *Fraser*: Go away you brute!
> *Dog*: Yurp, yurp!
> *Fraser*: Well sit down then and keep quiet. Say nothing and do nothing ... Hey! Give me that! Give it here, come on! Come on now, there's a good doggy. Open your mouth. That's the boy. Open. Wider, Wider. Wider for Uncle-wuncle Frazey-Wazey. Well, stone me, he's swallowed the bloody thing!
> *Dog:* Yurp, yurp!
> *Fraser*: Yurp yurp yourself and I hope it poisons you. Blast, I've cut myself now.

With all this chewing and swallowing going on Henry and I thought at first that the two of them might be passing messages to each other written on rice-paper. Later, when the curses and yelps took over, we wondered if they had been attacked by a rival gang and were having trouble keeping them at bay. And we particularly admired the way they finally reappeared from the fog, bloody but unbowed, and announced in the most matter-of-fact sort of drawl that they were ready to move off.

# 7

# Passing it By

Gentle reader, I have a confession to make. On this particular day of our walk we didn't manage to make contact with Offa's Dyke at all.

The fog had a lot to do with it, and all the rest of the blame lies squarely on the shoulders of King Offa. Henry said that if he could only find out what the hell he'd done with his maps he could have solved the problem for us in a matter of minutes, but we told him not to blame himself too much. We said that maps and guidebooks had a habit of disappearing just when they were most needed. They were famous for it, and most experienced travellers left them behind as a matter of principle. We said we were quite happy to rely on his sense of direction to pull us through. We said we couldn't imagine an eight-hour day going by without Henry leading us to a comfortable bed and a four-course meal at the end of it.

In the event we achieved the distinction of walking in an enormous half-circle around the town of Welshpool without having the least idea that it was there at all. The fog did lift for an hour in the early afternoon, but by that time we were on the other side of the hills and so far from habitation that we couldn't even see a road. But – and this bears out our faith in Henry's built-in survival instinct – we did find that bed and that meal more or less as we had imagined them.

Offa's Dyke was shallow enough where we had pitched camp. Two hundred yards further on we couldn't find it at all. There is a very good reason for this – it just isn't there. What on earth the good king thought he was doing dotting bits of dyke here and there along the Welsh border and then not joining them up with other bits of dyke I haven't the least idea. On the face of it, you can't get much dafter than that. As the ship's captain said when they forgot to weld on the plates beneath the water-line, it's all right as far as it goes – which is mostly in a downward direction.

Henry said it was probably absent-mindedness on Offa's part. I said No. For my money it was the same problem you get with all these state-run enterprises – lack of communication. 'You've done that twenty-mile stretch from Llanyardnooslyp to Glantyseidbach?' asks the Royal Seneschal of the Bedchamber. 'Yes we have, bach,' replies the Grand Artificer, vaguely wondering why they have started calling each other 'bach'. And then when the Welsh are pouring through the following summer, perpetrating here a rape, there a pillage, he says, 'Oh, *that* stretch! I thought you meant *that* one.' Then they peer at the plan by the light of the burning villages and try to work out where it was they went wrong.

Henry said, as we blundered along, that Offa is a very popular king among present-day history students. It seems that he is virtually unique among the great men of history inasmuch as only six things are known about him at all. One is a coin of some kind, one is Offa's Dyke, one is the fact that he died in either 749 or 750 AD – although how a man can be so vague as to forget which year he actually died in mystifies me. I don't know what the other three things are, but the point is that whatever essay the examiners try to set about King Offa everybody knows that the answer is going to have to be stitched together out of the six facts in one way or another. That's what makes it so easy. Of course, everyone is very clever at dressing those facts up to make them sound scholarly and high-falutin'. So you don't just say that somebody staggered into a field and picked up a coin which turned out to have Offa's name on it. You say that Offa had grasped the principle of monetary policy – it sounds better that way. And when you come to Offa's Dyke you say that he had grasped the principle of a negotiated frontier. In fact, apart from being vaguely born between 689 and 694 and vaguely dying some sixty years later, Offa seems to have spent most of the rest of his time in a state of almost permanent torpor, waking up every ten years or so to grasp another principle before dropping back into an exhausted slumber. All a result of the mead, I imagine.

Now you might think that a day spent walking around in an indeterminate semi-circle was a day wasted – but you would be wrong. On the contrary it was a day studded with interest. In the first place there was the question of Henry's feet. You know how it is. When things are going well and the sun is shining and you seem to be actively getting to where you set out to go to, nobody notices their feet at all. Then when you get lost and the wind turns cold and somebody points out to you that you're not six miles from journey's end but sixteen miles – (what a laughable mistake – how could anyone be so foolish, aha-ha!) – when all that happens you suddenly get attacked by a whole squadron of aches and pains you never noticed before. Well, Henry is particularly susceptible to these sorts of ailments.

I sometimes think that in the nineteenth century a whole lot of lives might have been saved if instead of putting canaries down coalmines to see whether there was an escape of gas they had put Henry down instead. He'd pick up the vibrations long before any canary started getting the tweety-weeties. Of course you may say that they'd never be able to fit Henry into a coalmine in the first place – but it's surprising what you can do with a spot of inventiveness. Slide him in headfirst would be the best method. Then you could support his feet on a trolley and roll him out again as soon as he got a whiff of danger.

Henry said his feet hurt and he wanted to do some bird-watching as soon as the fog lifted. Fraser said he believed both ends of the remark, but he didn't see why they should have to go together. 'You might as well say,' he said, 'I have two fags left in this packet and I want to move to Tunbridge Wells.'

This was provocative, and if Henry hadn't been concentrating on a slice of lemon meringue pie from his survival rations at the time he could well have taken it further. As it was, by the time he had finished his lunch we had been granted our short mid-afternoon break from the fog. Henry walked off to a low divan-shaped mound and lay with the binoculars to his eyes trying to look wise. Fraser and I sat at a respectful distance and philosophised about the theory and practice of birdwatching.

Fraser said there was nothing wrong with the practice of bird-watching. It was the theory that was all up the pole. It was a moot point, he said, whether Sigmund Freud or Charles Darwin had made the more disastrous contribution to modern science, but on the whole he tended to think that Darwin had managed to squeeze in by a short head. He said the whole idea of finches changing their beak-size to fit in with their environment was complete nonsense, together with all the rubbish about birds generally being descended from pterodactyls. If Darwin had bothered to ask anybody who knew about birds he could have found it out at first hand.

Fraser said he knew quite a lot about birds himself. His aunt had once kept one, and apart from that he quite often met them tearing up worms and mating and so forth when he came up the drive in his car.

Fraser said that all birds could be classified into three types: medium-sized brown, large black, and small coloured. Inside these three basic divisions nature had decreed that there should be a number of subsections. These didn't go around adapting themselves to their environment and developing alarm calls to ward off approaching bicycles. They just got on with the business of trying to scratch a decent living from the soil with the apparatus they had inherited.

'Take those birds you see wandering around in flocks on the seashore looking slightly silly,' Fraser said. 'In my book that is quite simply a medium-sized brown with webbed feet and a bobble on top. When you think about it nothing could be less adapted to walking about on a beach. Their bodies are so far away from their feet that they keep stubbing their toes on the rocks, and they haven't the first idea where the end of their beak is going because their eyes are in the side of their head. They are on that beach because that is where they have been put down and they just have to get on with it.

'Now so far as bird *watching* is concerned, it is a harmless enough activi –'

Fraser stopped abruptly because he saw he wasn't holding my attention. It was impolite of me I suppose to let my eyes wander like that, but I had just caught sight of something. I can't pretend to know much about bird-watching myself. Nothing at all in fact, but I think – or at least I *had thought* until I saw Henry – that one could reconstruct the basic elements simply enough. I mean to say, one expects to see a man at one end of the picture, and a bird at the other end, and (have I got it right?) the binoculars in the middle. What one doesn't often come across is a man lying down with his binoculars clapped to his eyes, and a thrush or medium-sized brown bird sitting on the crossbar of the binoculars whistling a happy tune as though it isn't sure whether it's Wednesday afternoon or Saturday morning. A picture like that suggests to me that the man in the tableau must be lying unnaturally still.

Fraser thought the same.

We crept up on the silent form of Henry from behind and carefully unwound his fingers from his field-glasses. His eyes were tight shut. We let him sleep on for about thirty seconds or so and then we thwacked him over the backside with a new lightweight camper's frying-pan of Scandinavian design.

Henry said afterwards that he had been awake all the time. He had merely closed his eyes so that he could memorise the markings of a particularly fine sparrow-hawk which he had been tracking for the last five minutes. But we heard no more moaning about sore feet from him for the rest of the day.

That was the first incident of note that happened that afternoon. The second occurred about an hour and a half later, although whether it was north, south, east or west of our lunchtime position I couldn't attempt to say. I couldn't say what sort of land we were on either because the fog had come down again so thick that Fraser had taken to beating it out of the way with his tweed hat to see if he could make anything out beyond. But gradually it began to dawn on us that we were not alone in this desolate place. Far in the distance, and from more than one direction at the same time, the quiet rumble of many engines seemed to be approaching us.

'Tanks,' said Henry wisely.

And he was right. And not just tanks. Soon we began to hear cries and the squelching of feet, and then one dim figure and then another in boots and combat dress ran straight across our noses without even bothering to look round. There's discipline for you. It's not every day that the fighting soldier has to carry out his manoeuvres around a trio of amateur antiquarians who are looking for Gallo-Saxon remains; yet these men took about as much notice of us as a pack of foxhounds would of a well-meaning spaniel that barked at them over a garden gate. I suppose when you've got thousands of men on the move you can't afford to hang around chatting to bystanders. Otherwise everybody starts getting themselves in the wrong place.

Eventually we found our way barred, head on, by a tank. The muzzle of it was quite visible – pointing nonchalantly at our heads, as a matter of fact. Then we could dimly make out the front of the tracks. The hole in the top where the voice came from, however, we couldn't see at all. Of course we could tell that the voice belonged to an officer, because they're the only ones allowed to use swear-words, and we had the distinct impression – though no very concrete evidence – that the face behind the voice was a bright purple colour.

He said: 'Where the bloody hell do you think you're going?'

We congratulated him on the question. We said it was just what we'd been asking ourselves since breakfast time. But this only seemed to make him crosser.

Fraser said that although we were completely lost we didn't want him to feel sorry for us because we were quite cheerful about it.

Henry asked him politely if he was lost too. Henry said that in spite of our predicament we were confident that we would somehow finish up with a bed and a hot meal, and we could probably manage to take him along as well provided he could slip away unobtrusively without telling the others.

Henry said, 'I don't think you've met my friend T. He's the one you can probably just make out if you squint down the gun barrel.'

Politeness pays off. You wouldn't believe how quickly those soldiers came clambering around us. They helped us into the tank and in next to no time they were whizzing and roaring us off through the fog. It must have been three or four miles that they carried us – more than an hour's walking when you think about it. Then they put us down on a pleasant little road and told us to be nice sensible people and not go wandering off in their direction again. And the officer very obligingly gave us a map reference like 39772443 – or it may have been 15605188 – which would have been terrifically helpful if only we had had a map. Then he saluted and about-turned and Fraser waved his hat in the air once more, and off they drove leaving us wondering which way to go next.

We had only walked on a matter of a hundred yards or so when we met a man standing by the roadside with a large knobbly stick. He was dripping with mist, and he wore wellington boots, and his face was small and pessimistic. He was in fact a farmer.

What a command of English that Welsh farmer had! It is rather humiliating when you think about it, but here was a man who wasn't even speaking his first language – at least I'm sure he wouldn't *admit* that English was his first language – yet there he stood mixing metaphors with zeugma and intertwining paradox with transference of epithet as though some of the great orators like Burke or Gladstone could take his correspondence course. And all on the subject of dead sheep.

You can imagine what a conversation of grunts and whistles you'd have with an English farmer about dead sheep.

'Arrm bin losin sheep.'

'Sleep?'

'Nar.'

'Nar what?'

'Nar. Sheep.'

'I see. You are losing sheep. Ye … s?'

'Ar.'

'Um … Why now have you been losing sheep – can it be foot-rot? The Common Agricultural Policy? Sheer neglect?'

'Nar.'

'Nar what?'

'Nar. Summat bin wurrinum.'

'Wurrinum, eh? Hold on now, let me guess. What *can* you mean?'

And so on.

Now with our farmer it was different. The angel Gabriel never spoke with greater eloquence than did he on the subject of sheep worrying. Far off in sunlit folds, it appeared, there grazed a race of sheep whose qualities both of mind and physique were so superior to the plodding lowland animals that all who saw them – and hundreds would make the pilgrimage year after year to do precisely that – exclaimed with wonder that such beauty and intelligence could be contained within the frame of a humble ewe, and many would fall down and give praise to the Great Being at whose behest the sheep had been ordained, quoting Goethe or Zechariah 13 : 7-9 in support of their tenet that this was indeed a flock apart from the common breed. Those who did not fall down and give praise, our farmer told us, mostly said eloquent things about the Meat Marketing Board.

There they sat – the sheep, I mean – suckling their young, and bleating to each other in tonic sol-fah. But – stay – what is this that has appeared in the bottom left-hand corner of the picture? No, no, it is not another of those houseflies which has landed on the frame from Mrs Jones's compost-heap next door. It is the sheep-worrying dog slavering nastily to itself as it works its way up the illustration, creeping from rock to rock with fell purpose, its fangs already red with the blood of rather less outstanding sheep that belong to other farmers in the neighbourhood. And now the hillsides are astir with a nameless unease. Across the sun a great cloud of mourning rolls as though to turn daylight into darkness in preparation for the shameless deed, and from the west a sighing wind cloaks the distracted bleating of the flock with an air of shrill lament.

Flee, flee, unguarded sheep! What use your bleatings now? Yet do not so. Was it not ever thus, that beauty stands defenceless before the envious eye of the marauder, that virtue gleams with a ray so pure that rock nor crag nor cave may hide her light from shining forth amid a world of evil!

He creeps, he crouches, he springs, and from the flock a fair ewe, the joy of her master's heart with a market value of £37.50, lies stricken. Another falls, and then another. Will the slaughter never end? Yes. Deep in the valley where the waters of the river Idris roll amid flowers, the goodly farmer has seen their plight and already he is across the stream and over the wall of the farthest penfold, a lithe and agile figure, small, but – like the youthful David – remarkably handsome in an odd sort of way and he's not armed with anything so daft as three small pebbles from the brook either, see. And now he is amongst his loved ones. See how they cluster around him for solace, while the killer turns tail in flight and streaks away across the hillside to its lair. Come ye to me my flock, for ye are my children! Come ye to me that are scattered abroad and ye shall find pasture! And let the hills lament, and let the high hills burst forth in lamentation, for ye that were an hundred-and-four score are now an hundred-and-seventy-and-seven, and of them that be lost there shall not one return, but among them that be saved there shall be joy upon their heads. And he that doeth this deed shall utterly perish.

Yea, I have sworn, and I have chosen my words carefully. He shall not last five minutes if I can only get my hands on him, boy. Yea, he shall die. And unto him that owneth him shall come forth a terrible bill for compensation.

It was a remarkable effort, and we told the farmer so. Henry said he particularly liked the bit about the change in the weather conditions prior to the assault. Of course the farmer was far too much of a professional to express any signs of pleasure at our compliments. Not for him a bowing and a smirking in front of the footlights. He just stood before us motionless, spitting on the ground from time to time and looking out bitterly into the fog as though questioning what atrocities might even now be going on out there.

When our applause had subsided he asked us if we would like to hear him on the topic of foot-and-mouth disease, but we declined. We said the emotional strain would be more than we could bear. But we cautioned him to be wary of letting his anger loose on any small black-and-white terrier that he might find, answering to – or rather not answering to – the name of Che. We said the dog had friends in high places. Given its busy agenda it was most unlikely that it could find time for anything as trivial as sheep-worrying. But it was not an animal to be trifled with, and any signs of hostility could well be answered by a fearful revenge.

This farmer's conversation had been accompanied by a good deal of gesticulation and hand-waving – the English are unique in not using their hands to talk with – and from this manual side of his discourse we had gained the information that his own farm lay down the valley: that is, away from the way we were going. I must say that this came as some relief, because as we had walked up to him we had been wondering to ourselves whether we might not be spending the night at his house. Now we were spared the need to enquire. So we walked on, and a mile further up the road we came upon a rickety sign and a track leading off to our left. The rickety sign said Pontbedr Farm, and the track was muddy and showed signs of daily use. We turned up it and began to prepare our minds for the awkward task of asking for a night's lodging – awkward to us and probably more awkward still for our hosts.

I said that at least we would be staying with genuine Border people.

Henry said that could be a mixed blessing. He said he didn't mean it unkindly, but he had had one or two experiences of staying with genuine people, and the trouble about them was that they usually turned out to be a bloody sight more genuine than you'd bargained for.

He said he'd had his initial baptism of fire when he'd just turned eighteen and took himself off to Greece for two months to get to know the people at first hand. Henry's father, who never travelled anywhere as a matter of principle, said it would be much better if he got to know them at second hand, but Henry insisted and off he went.

For the first ten days apparently Henry had a rapturous time. He walked the hills of Central Greece exulting in the clear Mediterranean air and eating enormous meals of mutton and cheese, which seemed to cost next to nothing in the remoter villages. Then one day as he was sitting down exulting under an olive tree he was joined in the cool of the shade by a statuesque girl who was barefooted and carrying a water bottle on her head. She poured Henry a cup of water and he gave her a piece of bread, and together they sat laughing and joking through the afternoon.(That at least is Henry's story, and I can imagine from the girl's point of view that if Henry ever succeeded in cracking any joke in Greek she was bound to find it pretty laughable.) She was shy and twinkling-eyed, and about an hour after she'd walked on Henry realised that she'd taken his wallet. When he turned out his pockets the only thing he had left of any significance was his airline ticket home dated four weeks hence.

Henry said he could always have made his way back to Athens and changed the flight back to an earlier date. But he still didn't want to leave Greece, and besides he couldn't bear the thought of his father's grinning face when he met him off the plane. So he resolved on a different – a more genuine – course.

High up above his head as he lay there on the grass Henry could see the white dome of a monastery perched like a gull's nest on the edge of a mountain. By nightfall he had made his way to it, and after what must have been a bewildering mimeshow for the abbot and a number of senior monks he managed to get it into their heads that he intended to book in for a long stay. Henry said he got the impression that they thought he was mad, and the idea seemed to go around the table – he didn't know this, of course, but he sort of sensed it – that anybody who wanted to stay with them must need his head examining, and on that basis they had better take pity on him and let him in.

Henry said that the reason for all this amazement on the part of the inmates only dawned on him late the next afternoon. It seemed that his arrival had more or less coincided with the start of Greek Orthodox Lent. From his first day till the time he had to leave they had three meals per day, each consisting of eighteen dried peas and a glass of water. The monks themselves absolutely loathed it. The abbot loathed it too, and he used secretly to invite Henry into his room and win his peas off him by beating him at some peculiar game of cards which Henry could never understand the rules of. Henry couldn't complain, of course, because he was afraid he might be thrown out. By the time he got home, Henry said, he was a shadow of his former self.

'And that,' said Henry, as the forbidding silhouette of the farmyard surged suddenly into view, 'that is why the search for genuineness should never be carried to excess.'

'Still', said Henry, as we tolled at a rather handsome and well-polished brass bellpull. 'Any port in a storm.'

A small girl of about eleven answered the door, and we explained our predicament. She asked us to come in. In the hall she stopped suddenly and said that she was at a loss to know what best to do. We were most welcome to stay for the evening, of course – that went without saying. The question was that, since there was nobody to introduce us, she hoped we wouldn't consider it too much of a gaffe if she simply announced herself. Her name was Armandine Elton-Willis. Her parents were out for the moment at a meeting of the local multi-racial Playgroup Committee, and she herself was rather tied up with homework. However, she was sure she could find us a slice of quiche in the fridge to keep us going till dinner time.

Armandine Elton-Willis said that her brother Traquair normally went to bed early, being only little. If we wouldn't mind waiting for a moment she'd go up to his cot and see if she could find the *Guardian* crossword. There was usually quite a bit of the puzzle left to do, and it might just keep us amused for a few minutes until she was free to join us herself.

In a way we were very grateful.

In another way we were thoroughly dissatisfied.

# 8

# Keeping it Up

Next morning we got a lift. It was Mr Elton-Willis's idea – he was just setting out for his Saturday-morning jog when the three of us got downstairs. He said he had to go into Welshpool soon after nine to pick up the newspapers and it would be the easiest thing in the world to run us on to where the Dyke starts up again.

We discussed it briefly over our farmhouse breakfast of bran and yoghurt. I wasn't in favour. It seemed to me that if we had walked off the right path we could walk back on to it again, but Fraser said with somebody like Henry as a guide that didn't necessarily follow. Fraser said what was he going to tell his grandchildren in years to come when they asked him about Offa's Dyke and all he'd done was to go round and round the same hillside for days on end.

Henry said: 'If I were you I'd blame everyone else. You usually do.' But, he said, Offa's Dyke was the objective, and all in all he was for getting back on to it by the quickest possible means.

So I was outvoted, and Mr Elton-Willis kindly drove us through Welshpool in his little Lancia and across the Severn, which lies just beyond, and down through the hamlet of Buttington to the point where the Dyke begins. Mark you, we knew we were coming to it quite a bit before, because of the numbers of weekend-hikers all making for the same spot.

Oh how I hate them, those weekend-hikers. You can tell the weekend-hiker a mile off by his shiny knees and his silly bobble hat and the shrill excited pitch of his voice as he rediscovers long-forgotten novelties like grass and thistles. Normally he will have a wife in tow who seems, of all loony things, to be starting a collection of dead bracken – that at least is what she appears to be pulling out of the hedgerows and burdening the rest of the family with. Then, of course, there is the child. He, in terms of character, comes out of it as the best of the group. Surly, square, and with a marked tendency to lag behind, he can't see why he's been hauled out on this bloody walk in the first place. His day would have been much better spent squashing beetles behind the garage at home, which is exactly what he'd planned to do before they sprang this route march on him. But that's adults all over. You just get yourself organised to do something really interesting, and bang, the next minute you find yourself attached to some labour-gang or other.

'Darling!' the husband will exclaim, pausing for breath after the first seventy yards or so and peering indeterminately into the hedge. 'Darling, do you see what I see?'

'What, darling, what?' cries his wife gustily as she closes in on him. 'Oh, do hurry up, Bobby, my pet,' she urges the child behind her. 'Come and see what Daddy's seen.'

'Wotz 'e seen then?' says the child without quickening his pace. 'Wotz Daddy seen then?'

'He's seen a … what is it you've seen, darling?'

'Look there!'

'Where?'

'You see that branch, darling?'

'Yes, darling.'

'Well, follow it along with your eye and tell me if you see something surprising.'

'Er … let me think. Um … is it above or below the fork?'

'Silly darling!' exclaims the husband in triumph. 'It *is* the fork. Don't you see. The branch forks three ways at the same time. You don't often see that on a branch now, do you?'

Even to a wife who is prepared to get excited about some pretty low-interest-level material to keep the family enthusiasm bubbling along, this seems to be borderline stuff from the point of view of stimulating the rebellious Bobby.

'Daddy's seen a tree,' she tells him, trying to keep it short, as he comes up.

'Yeah?' says the child. 'Wot a load of crap.'

For this remark the child receives a series of cuffs around the head from his mother together with a torrent of motherly abuse. 'How dare you (thwack) use such language in front of your father (thwack). You ought to be ashamed of yourself (thwack, thwack). Where do you pick up these foul expressions, that's what I want to know (thwack). Is that the sort of guttersnipe remark they teach you at school (thwack, thwack, thwack). Now look,' she says accusingly, 'there's somebody coming. Stop snivelling and pull yourself together. You're not hurt.'

'I am 'urt.'

'No you're not. Blow your nose and stop making an exhibition of yourself.'

'I uvn't gdda 'nkerchief.'

'Here's mine. Now, these people are coming. Good afternoon!' she calls desperately to the approaching party.

'Good afternoon,' they murmur back, giving her a wide berth. They have been studying her wrist-action for the last thirty yards or so, and each of them has decided to himself that this is certainly a severe case of child battering, probably murder. On the other hand they don't feel it's for them to interfere, so they've each taken a mental note of her description just in case the police should put out a call for witnesses later on.

'Darling!' rings back the little-boy-blue voice of her unbearable husband from a hundreds yards up the hedgerow. 'Darling, I think I've found something else now! Believe it or not I think it may be a lapwing.'

Not all weekend-hikers are as bad as that. Some on the other hand are a good deal worse. Take for example the man who fell in with us for the first ten miles beyond Welshpool. He was alarmingly hearty and glowing with enthusiasm, of course – but all weekend-hikers over the age of little Bobby are like that. It was the mindless series of questions that wore us down. It seemed, talking to him – and it was impossible to *avoid* talking to him – that there was no answer that the human brain could devise that didn't give rise to yet another fatuous question: if not to an immediate question, then at least to an exclamation of wonder and delight, which was if anything worse.

'Tell me,' he said to Henry about six-and-a-half seconds after he had caught up with us. 'Tell me, what do you do for a living?'

Henry said, 'I'm a statistician.'

'Really?' exclaimed our companion. 'How very interesting.'

See what I mean? Now if he had said how totally dull and boring an occupation being a statistician must be, one could have had some respect for the man. If he had coughed nervously and changed the subject on to growing your own courgettes one would have sympathised with his predicament. But to go around shouting 'How interesting' when a man tells you he's a statistician is a sure sign that you are – to use a medical expression – soft in the head.

'How very interesting,' he went on. 'I should think you've seen a lot of changes in statistics in the last few years, haven't you?'

'Yes,' Henry said. Well – there again – he was hardly going to say that he hadn't, was he? He was hardly going to say that he just pulls open a drawer and gets out the statistics for 1979 and blows the dust off them and changes the date and bungs them straight in the post.

'Ah yes,' said the man. 'Yes. New methods coming in too, I shouldn't wonder. Tell me do you use computers much?'

'Yes,' said Henry. 'Quite a bit of the time.'

'Quite a bit of the time, eh?'

'Yes,' said Henry.

'Quite a bit of the time, but not all of the time is that it?'

'That's it,' said Henry.

'Would you say,' said the man probingly, 'that you use computers almost fifty per cent of the time?'

'More than that probably,' said Henry.

'*More* than that. My word. There's progress for you. How much more would you say – just a little bit more, or quite a lot more?'

'It depends what the job is,' said Henry very sensibly.

'*Ah*!' said the man, as if he had put his finger on the critical point he had been searching for, although of course there was no point to his conversation at all. 'It *depends*, doesn't it? Yes I can see that all right. Tell me now, do you really think – I mean, do you yourself really think that statistics are useful? What I mean is, do you really think that they help us out here in the modern world?'

'I suppose so,' said Henry dully.

'You do? Fascinating. Now look,' said the man. 'Suppose I

were to ask you for a set of statistics on ... on ... what shall we say?'

'Hedgehogs,' said Fraser quickly, trying to come to Henry's rescue.

'Hedgehogs – that's an idea!' said the man enthusiastically. 'Hedgehogs!' And, meandering away from his point rather like a hedgehog himself, he turned to Fraser and continued babbling. 'Hedgehogs – what an intriguing suggestion. Tell me, why did you say hedgehogs?' And so on.

We took him in relays, this searcher after knowledge. First Henry had him, of course. Then Fraser surged in and carried him on for the next mile. Then he was tossed to me still exclaiming and marvelling and full of pep, and after I had run with him for twenty minutes or so, Henry would close in on us and take him over again. That's how we shared the work. We tried him on a number of topics. Not ordinary common-or-garden topics, mark you, but the pettiest, drabbest, most dismally uninteresting little topics we could lay our hands on. Things like how to patch linoleum, and the effects of the baked-bean industry on pre-war Ilford. And Fraser even went to the lengths of describing a football match he had once watched between Army Pay Corps 'B' and an invitation side from the Hosiery Trade where the score was nil-nil after extra time. And to all this our friend responded with ever-increasing delight and curiosity. 'Really!', 'How splendid!', 'Tell me, what do you think would be the normal number of throw-ins in an amateur soccer match?'

We finally shook him off a mile or so south of Montgomery using a trick in which the Government or the Countryside Commission or some such body certainly had an important hand.

Now, I'm not a man normally to go around proclaiming how tricks are done. The way I see it, it isn't fair to the conjurer. When he's just pulled a rabbit out of the hat, I mean to say, it does rather spoil the party to dash up and lift the false bottom out of the thing, revealing three coloured handkerchiefs, a couple of pigeons and a cobra all curled up inside waiting for their chance to come on stage. But in the case of the Waymark Path Trick – that is what this particular trick is called – I think I can in confidence reveal it to you. Otherwise I don't see how the Government is going to get the recognition it deserves when it has to spend so much of the time defending itself against malicious and usually quite misdirected abuse.

The point about the Waymark Path Trick is this. The Government takes a perfectly ordinary path which people may want to walk along like the Lyke Wake Walk (which we've mentioned before) or Offa's Dyke, and it thinks to itself how it can preserve that path for people of culture and distinction like you and me, while sending all the weekend-hikers and the dreadful vanilla-flavoured-crisp-packet crew off on some quite different excursion without feeling they've been hard done by. The answer they've come up with goes as follows: along the general direction of the proper Dyke or Walk, but running, say, a mile or two off to one side they create a new and quite spurious track which they call the Waymark Path. They call it the Waymark Path because as soon as they've worked out where it's going to go they send lots of little men off with brushes and pots who mark the way for everybody with attractive green acorns which are stuck on to fences and the trunks of trees. Then they ring up the printers and rush out a whole series of booklets telling people how much better it is than the real thing, and finally just for good measure they install a resting area or a forest toilet, every twenty miles or so so that the public feels it's got something to aim for. Of course these Waymark Paths are no easy thing to plan, and from time to time they do have to run them where the real Dyke actually goes; and it was just at the point where the two routes separate that we managed to work ourselves free from our companion.

'Do you think you're allowed to go that way?' he said as he watched us crossing the barbed-wire fence to the freedom of the continuing Dyke.

'No,' we told him cheerfully. 'We're trespassing. It's got to be illegal.'

'But what if you're caught?'

'We'll be run in,' I said.

'Run in,' said Fraser, 'or shot.'

'Shot,' said Henry, as he unsnagged his trouser-leg from the wire. 'That's the likeliest thing.'

'Amazing,' said our friend. 'What'll you say to that?'

'Now that,' said Henry, 'depends on how many of us are left to tell the tale.'

When we last looked back at him he was still standing there two hundred yards or so away. He had the appearance of a man who feels that there are a lot of questions left unanswered.

As far as the business of trespassing goes there are two kinds of trespassing: honest trespassing, as I call it, and the other kind. From the honest trespasser's point of view there is very little that can't be achieved provided he is prepared to resort to manly apology where necessary and the occasional bolt for cover behind a gorse bush. This sort of trespassing is nothing more than the plain man's way of getting his own back on all the farmers who fill in the time they have left over after claiming their government grants by ploughing up the Rights of Way across their land. Fair game, if you ask me. Che Woofera obviously thought so too, because – seeing that lunchtime was coming on – he suddenly joined us by scampering down the bank and then proceeded to trip all three of us up in as many minutes by way of a hint that it was time to take a break.

We have now reached the point in our story where we came closest to crossing paths directly with the original *Three Men in a Boat*. I refer to the matter of opening tins. You remember in *Three Men in a Boat* how J. and Harris and George decided to treat themselves to a tin of pineapple chunks and then they found that they hadn't got a tin-opener. They bashed and banged that tin about, and they attacked it with the boat-hook, and all they succeeded in doing was knocking it into a shape so leering and ghostly that they eventually took fright and tossed the tin – pineapple and all – into the river.

Well, we had our incident with a tin now, although since it was a sardine tin a tin-opener, of course, didn't come into it. You've probably noticed that sardine tins have changed quite a lot in the last few years. Gone are the days of the old roll-back-the-lid-with-a-key model where you used traditionally to cut your finger with the first attempt and then found you'd put the key in the wrong way round and couldn't get it off, and finally you finished the job with a pair of pliers. Our tin – jumbo size of course – was the new insert-finger-in-ring-and-simply-pull-back variety.

Fraser was doing the pulling, and Henry and Che and I were sitting watching him casually on the top of the bank, not forseeing any difficulties, if you know what I mean.

Then it went:

> Pull! ... nothing happened.
> Pull! ... nothing happened.
> A-one, a-two, a-three – Pu ... ll!

Suddenly to our mild surprise Fraser was no longer with us, although from the sound of his voice coming up from below we understood that he was alive and well and living in the bottom of a ditch.

Henry, who is remarkably quick in an emergency, managed to catch hold of the tin, and began to study it closely to make sure it was still intact. From down below Fraser clearly felt that Henry had got his priorities wrong and that it was *he* we ought to be checking over for cuts and abrasions; but then as Henry pointed out he wasn't qualified to check Fraser over – wouldn't know a broken bone if you showed him one – whereas he gave ground to no one in his ability to pass judgment on a sardine tin.

What had happened of course was that the ring had come off, leaving an absolutely regular tin with no means of getting inside it. Round the top face we could distinctly see the line where the pullaway section joined on to the rest. The only thing was, there wasn't anything left to pull at.

We examined the problem. Che was for taking it away and having the thing opened by experts who knew what they were doing. 'Give it to me,' he said, 'and I'll have the thing sorted out before you can say "fish". I've got a bunch of lads in the woods back there who can eat this sort of problem for breakfast.'

We said No. We said eating it for breakfast was just what we were afraid of. Henry suggested a tin-opener, but I pointed out that it wouldn't go round the corners. I said that if we took that route we'd be left with a leaky tin, but not a tin we could open and eat.

At this point Fraser thrust his head back over the bank and came up with one of his rare ideas. At least it seemed like an idea until we tried it out and saw what actually happened. He said that if the lid was designed to lift off it followed logically that it must also be capable of being pressed in. At first glance, he said, you might think that this would squash the fish inside, but in practice he calculated there would be little damage. 'With any luck,' he told us, 'we'll get away with a slight displacement of fluid, nothing more. The important thing is to apply a steady even pressure.'

Henry and Che and I retired to one side and watched him from a distance. 'If there's going to be any displacement of fluid,' we said to each other, 'we'd rather it didn't displace itself over us.'

Fraser faced the ditch this time. A man can roll over backwards easily enough, but with his feet spread out in front of him he is not going to topple over forwards.

It went like this:

Press! ... nothing happened.
Press! ... nothing happened.
A-one, a-two, a-three – Pre ... ss!

With a long even *phlumph*, twelve sardines and what seemed to be a surprising amount of tomato ketchup spurted up into the air, over the edge of the parapet, and sploshed down into the Dyke beyond, with Che Woofera about three seconds behind them in pursuit. I think the dog had some idea that they might swim away.

We got out some biscuits and cheese, and while we were eating them we waved *au revoir* to Che who saluted us in a preoccupied way from the opposite bank before galloping off over the western skyline. As far as I know he caught all twelve sardines, because when we'd finished our alternative lunch some twenty minutes later we went down and looked for them, but not one of those sardines could we see.

The stretch of Dyke from south of Montgomery to the Clun Hills where we spent the night is a brave and exciting ten miles or so, full of stiff slopes up and down. Mostly – from the walker's point of view – it seems to be up, of course, because for the greater part of the time you are struggling around the side of Edenhope Hill (1,350 ft). Oxygen seems scarce up there for the plain man like myself whose normal idea of exercise is the steady even stroll across the carpet to the television set. One gets to thinking deep thoughts, like what the hell am I doing on this jaunt in the first place, and how am I going to describe all these acres of solid scenery to my readers without getting them to flip over the next five pages with cries of 'Boring, boring!' In fact, come to think of it, what deep moral stance ought I to take up over the question of descriptions in the first place?

When I first started out on this book Widget took a strong line with me on the subject of description. She said: 'Cut it out.' She said nobody ever read Jerome K. Jerome's descriptions. She said life is too short nowadays for all that stuff about the piper at the gates of dawn and the perfume of the beech nuts wafting across to you from the small island in the stream – or was she getting mixed up with *The Wind in the Willows*? Anyway, I know what she means. Besides, when dawn breaks over you in a three-man tent, the only perfume likely to come wafting across is from Henry's socks, which he insists on keeping on in bed and then pushing through the hole in the bottom of his sleeping-bag and wiggling around in front of your face when you've woken up too early and are trying to get back to sleep again.

On the other hand that's just Widget's point of view. There may be people, in fact I hope there are, who would give their eye teeth for a nice meaty description: the sort of people who like to have it roll over them in chunks. And, of course, one must consider the author, who has the problem – if you look at it from my angle for a moment – of indicating the passage of time on a long afternoon's slog without distasteful resort to talking about Henry's breathing habits or Fraser's strange choice of words when he trips up and falls in a puddle.

So what we shall do is this. We shall turn, dear reader, and look back from our vantage point on the hillside across the Vale of Severn, and we shall assume for the purposes of the exercise that the twin towns of Welshpool and Montgomery are both in our sights and we shall give a reasonably brief and imaginative description of them, and then we shall sort of pan the thing round and bring it back to where we are standing.

In point of fact our description of Welshpool and Montgomery has got to be brief and imaginative because I don't know the first thing about either of 'em. You will recall that the only sidelong glance we got at Welshpool was when Mr Elton-Willis very nicely nipped through it with us in the back of his car. And as far as Montgomery is concerned, we would almost certainly have slipped into *that* for a cup that cheers round about eleven o'clock, if it hadn't been for the fact that we had that talkative idiot with us at the time, and we needed his pubside prattle like we needed concrete boots. All this is to your advantage, however, gentle reader, because it means we can launch into a full flood of soul on the subject of Welshpool and Montgomery without having our minds cluttered by any preconceived ideas.

Ahem.

The towns of Welshpool and Montgomery are both much of a muchness. Oh, yes. It is quite common for citizens of Welshpool to walk into Montgomery and vice-versa and ask to see the Bank Manager or something like that and then find out that they are in the wrong town and say, 'Is this Montgomery? Well, stack me! I thought it was Welshpool.' Both boroughs were of early foundation, but that needn't bother us because they were smashed up so frequently and systematically in the border wars that it wasn't till Tudor times that people started putting cement in between the bricks in the hope that the houses might actually be allowed to stand up. In the late sixteenth century they petitioned the Crown for a royal charter, an event which gave rise to Queen Elizabeth's much publicised 'You've got to be joking' remark, and after that they settled down into a sort of sedate decorum and gradually filled up with firms of Chartered Accountants and Solicitors with names like Orle, Mowth, and Trosiers, and Bickerstaff and Poss. So much for history.

Culture is a particular forte in these border boroughs. Each town has successfully stumbled into a twinning arrangement with a different continental municipiality, and once a year they astonish the visiting burgemeester with the quality of the British sherry at council receptions. Then they entertain him to a Mendelssohn selection arranged for harmonica ensemble, and put him back on the plane at Birmingham clutching a Caerphilly cheese.

The view from the south west is possibly the most striking in both cases. Tourists exclaim at the prospect of Balaclava Villas from across the tennis courts, but there is nothing much the Council can do about it because the disused gasworks is on private land and although the metalwork may have a scrap value, what's it going to cost to take it all down and store it somewhere? The excursion to the Alderman Gladbag Municipal Reservoir high up in the hinterland between the two towns is much favoured by taxi drivers.

Increased supermarket penetration is currently being installed, and a particularly complex multi-storey carpark complex is promised to be completed by the end of next year. The work at the moment is seven months ahead of schedule. Both places boast a small and expanding industrial estate. At least the estate is expanding and if anybody can find any industry that wants to go to it they should ring the Town Hall direct and reverse the charges.

As we leave these two little towns nestling refulgently amid the verdant pasturage of the placid borders, we continue our search for adjectives in a southerly direction until we reach the first slopes of the little foothills that beckon us onwards towards Clun Peak and the distant Black Mountains. Oh, what a wealth of interest surrounds us here! Here famed Offa, Saxon warlord, constructed one of the sections of his famed Dyke through the grounds of the famed Mellington Hall Hotel. Here Alwyn Morfa, genius before his time, gave birth in 1643 to the brilliant but never-recognised Morfe Code, only he couldn't come up with a satisfactory buzzer. Nor can we forget Lloyd George, though we may try. Who would not linger here amid these grassy slopes listening to the call of the lark far up in the puff-ball sky, or watching the effortless flight of the medium-sized brown curlew as, carolling to her lover, she wheels in dizzy spirals towards the sunset and her craggy nest? Nature is all around us. Far off from out his woodland hollow the grey form of the shaggy badger lumbers blinking into the dusk and bumps into a stoat that happens to be passing which in turns rolls over and slightly squashes a dormouse. Then they all apologise. And amid all this harmony and burgeoning of nature, how small, how infinitely small does man appear.

Ah man, man! The wrecker and destroyer. The scourge of animals and of the green things of the earth. There is no place for you in such tranquillity. What right have you to break the peace with which Nature herself has bound the temples of her children? You with your engines and your noise and your busy empty bustle – get you gone. Turn you aside and leave the earth to nurture her own. Away, away to some other place – and there take you what rest you may from troubled thoughts and from vain and futile activities, and let the down of sweet slumber touch the eyelids of the innocent ones.

As a matter of fact Henry and Fraser and I were more or less following that advice just as the sun was beginning to show signs of packing it in for the evening. Fraser had been walking along the top of the bank – he was finding the bottom a bit damp underfoot – and being a sharp-eyed lad he noticed six or seven tents in a paddock off to our right. Some small camp-site, we surmised. Nor were we wrong. It was the Cwm Mawr Farm Campsite. 'Hot water, eggs, bread, and milk available indoors.' And a few minutes later, after the traditionally vindictive haggle over whether we were paying four pounds or four pounds twenty-five, we found ourselves a spot under a tree, got the tent up, and settled down to prepare the evening meal.

# 9

# Putting it Across

A very unfunny thing happened to us around suppertime that night.

It wasn't the meal as such. That was fine – an enormous baked-bean omelette cooked by Fraser. And it wasn't the Swedish frying-pan either. *That* hopeless thing simply had to be abandoned. It's all very well designing these ultra-lightweight utensils for the fast-moving camper, but when they can't even take a playful impact with the seat of a man's trousers without buckling up like a hub-cap it's time to get back to the proper job. So as far as that was concerned we simply borrowed another one from a tent across the way where the woman was cooking stew and didn't need it.

No. It was the Lurking Druid that got us. He was in fact the husband of the woman who lent us the frying-pan, but I don't think it's fair to blame the fellow on her.

You know how it is on camp-sites – or, if you don't, I'll tell you. In the main they are very decent places and they attract a very self-respecting cross-section of the community, who get on with their own business, and are polite and tolerant, and try not to get in each other's way. That's how most people are. But on every camp-site, however small, there is always one obsessional pest of a person who is there from ulterior motives. He is the man who wants to talk to you about something. Well, he doesn't want to talk to *you* specifically. He wants to have a go at anybody he can back into a corner and get to listen. I suppose the reason why he frequents these spots is that he has so numbed and antagonised everybody back home that he has to go out and find a fresh audience in the most obvious place that comes to mind.

Now the obsession, of course, can vary, but the techniques for foisting it on you don't change much. There is the man with the moan, and the man wants to show you the hand-made shelving in his caravan; and there is the man who has worked out a scheme for re-processing lobsters and feeding them to reindeer. But whatever his particular cause you can usually pick him out by the predatory way he hangs around your tent waiting for an opportunity to swoop in and bore you to tears. I say you can pick him out, but can you short of physical brutality, or downright abuse, actually fend him off?

Ah! *That* is the question. Usually there is some sort of tit-for-tat that you can organise.

In our case we knew we'd got a right one from the start, of course, by the brazen way he just walked across with his own camp stool and a 'How's the frying-pan doing?', which was all he bothered himself with by way of an explanation for muscling in on us.

'Strangers in these parts, I take it?' he barged on, not that it would have mattered if we'd said No. In fact I think we probably did.

We looked him up and down: the loose mouth hanging open ready for action, the carefully arranged locks, the knobbly knees covered by a hide like a rhinoceros's.

Then he began. He told us his name was Jackson, a London solicitor – 'At least,' he said, 'I used to be, until I retired and fell in love with this place. Of course,' he continued, 'Daphne and I had been to Wales many times before I retired – don't get me wrong. More and more as the years went by, as a matter of fact. And then one evening we were sitting at home and I said to her, "Daphne?" – "Yes, John?" – I said, "Daphne, do you know what's going through my mind?" And she said "You're going to tell me that you want to retire and go and live in Wales." Just like that. Wasn't that an extraordinary thing?'

'It depends how often you'd tried it on her before,' said Fraser.

'– Oh, you may talk,' went on the London solicitor, getting his voice into top form. 'You may talk of France, or Spain, or the Alps, or the Grand Canyon for that matter. All very beautiful places in their way, I haven't a doubt. But when you get to know a country, and a people, and a language, as I have done, I'll tell you this, you may walk from the North Pole to the South and at the end of the day you'll still come back here and say to yourself "This is my spot!" '

There was a pause. 'D'you know much of history?' he added suddenly, judging the throw-away delivery to perfection.

We gave this some serious thought – looking for a way out, so to speak.

Fraser said, 'Plenty for the time being', which wasn't a bad effort. I think both sides knew we were coming to some sort of crunch. Jackson had produced an enormous pipe – a good twenty-five minutes' worth – and he was already beginning to fill it up, wearing a dreadful leer of triumph.

Then, 'Did you ever hear the story,' he said, leaning forward confidentially and putting his hand on his knee. 'Did you ever hear the story of Blodwedd, Princess of Powys?'

Fraser said, 'No, thank God', and Jackson said he wanted to tell it to us now. He said it was one of the most moving little stories we would ever hear in our lives. Fraser said in that case if he could let him have it in writing together with a stamped addressed envelope he'd promise him a full opinion within a fortnight. Jackson laughed in a battle-scarred sort of way, and said that the Welsh bardic tradition was entirely by word of mouth and that a story could vary sometimes quite fantastically at the whim of the teller. Fraser said could he give us a timescale for this particular whim, and Jackson said that once he got into it time wouldn't seem to make any difference at all. He said that we would have to forgive him if he occasionally used the odd phrase in Welsh – he was so used to thinking of this charming tale in Welsh that he would inadvertently let it slip into its natural language from time to time – it was a curious trait of his that he didn't seem to be able to throw off.

Fraser said, 'Get on with it.'

Of all the daughters of Maerdrach, King of Powys [Jackson said], none was more fair than the Princess Blodwedd. The King had seven daughters and five sons, and each of them he loved as dearly as himself, but if there was one who captivated his heart more than all the others then Blodwedd the youngest was surely she. Sometimes he would call her his *pwentll nant*, his little daughter of the morning rose. At other times, when the tawny rays of the dying sun would touch her cheeks with its glowing embers as she ran skipping over the hillsides, he would give her the nickname *myrla myn*, elf of the firelight. But most of all he called her *tantynas*, that is to say 'joy at the last'. 'For,' said the King, 'whatever woes shall furrow this fair brow, she shall at the last find joy and contentment.' Thus they lived [Jackson pressed on grimly] in peace and happiness for many years.

Now it happened one day that Princess Blodwedd rose early when it was just light and left her father's castle, and tripped like the haze upon the dew down to the river's edge to bathe herself in the clear waters. And there upon a rock –

'Bathe herself?' queried Fraser.
'Yes,' Jackson said.

In the clear waters. And there upon a r –

'Lack of facilities back at the motte and bailey?'
'If you care to put it that way.

And there upon a r –

'This seems odd,' said Fraser. 'We know, of course that hygiene arrangements in former centuries had not developed to the pitch of mania that we suffer from today. None the less a castle without water inside its walls is a castle which is going to prove distinctly vulnerable in time of siege.'

'No doubt,' Jackson said. 'But I'm not suggesting that the castle didn't have a well. I merely made it clear that the princess preferred the privacy and seclusion of the running stream.'

'Privacy? I wouldn't call larking starkers within a bowshot of the battlements *privacy* exactly.'

'With you around it wouldn't be,' said Jackson nastily. 'But in that age of beauty and innocence things were different.'

'The sentries didn't look, you mean?'

'Precisely.'

'I merely asked for information,' said Fraser. 'Please continue.'

And there upon a rock where she would often sit on summer mornings, she gazed into the crystal stream and combed her hair and braided it with the white lilies that bounce and bobble in the swirling flood. And as she reached out to pluck the whitest lily of them all, it chanced that her foot slipped and the foaming tide received her and carried her away, as though to sweep her to the nethermost part of the stream the end of which is known to no man.

But, as good fortune would have it, scarcely the length of a swallow's flight from the rock two woodcutters were battening their fire beside the river's brim. And the elder woodcutter said to his son: 'Son, my eyes are old, and moreover it is not yet clear day. Tell me, what see you that floats towards us, so silvery white along the stream?' And the son shaded his eyes against the morning ray and said, 'Father, it is a milk-white swan, the whitest you have ever seen. Shall I swim out and fetch it, Father?' And his father said, 'No. No son of mine shall dare that stream, though it be for the whitest swan that swims upon water.'

And the father looked at the river a second time, and said to his son: 'Son, my eyes are old, and moreover it still lacks something of a true light. Look again, I pray you, and tell me what it is that floats towards us so silvery white along the stream.' And the son stood beneath the bough of a great oak to shield his eyes against the morning ray and said: 'Father, it is a milk-white ewe, the whitest you have ever seen. Shall I swim out and fetch it, Father?' And his father said: 'No. No son of mine shall dare that stream, though it be for the whitest ewe that ever gave suck.'

And the father looked at the river a third time and said to his son: 'Son, my eyes are old, and though it be clear day look once more, I pray you, and tell me what it is that floats so silvery white along the stream.' And the son lay down beneath the leaves of the great laurel which gives more shade than all the trees of the wood, and he said: 'Father, it is a milk-white maiden, the whitest and the fairest you have ever seen. Shall I swim out and fetch her, Father?' And the father said: 'Swim, and the blessings of my heart be upon you. For he is no son of mine who shall not dare that stream for such a maiden.'

'Yes,' said Jackson, 'What is it now?'

'Who, me?' Fraser said.

'Yes. You said something.'

'N … o. I just breathed heavily.'

'Emotion probably,' I said.

'Call it that,' said Fraser, 'For want of a better word.'

Jackson cleared his throat, with the sound of a metal worker rasping off a rough edge, and battered on.

So the boy swam out, and he clasped the Princess Blodwedd by her hand whiter than lilies, and he guided her to the farther bank and laid her down upon the soft grass of the meadow. And presently she opened her eyes, and she saw the comely face of the youth gazing down upon her own. And she said to him: 'Good youth, you who have saved me from the turbulent stream, tell me what recompense I can give you, and I shall go to my father and ask it of him, and surely he will grant it you though it were half his kingdom.'

And the youth replied: 'As for kingdoms and as for half-kingdoms I know nothing of these things. But if your father should find it in his heart to give me your hand, that would be more recompense to me than any treasure I could name.'

Now when she heard these words the heart of the Princess Blodwedd gave a bound within her, for in all Powys she had not seen a youth so brave of stature or so fair of complexion. And she said: 'Gladly will I ask this thing, and as my father loves me he will not refuse it.'

'Go then,' said the youth. 'Only remember this. Today I must go on a long journey into a distant kingdom where I must reside for seven long years until I may return again. Wait patiently therefore against my coming back, and when I return, then shall you give me your hand in marriage.'

So it was agreed. And Blodwedd returned to her father's castle, and she told her father all that had happened and how she had pledged her hand to the young woodcutter who had saved her from the turbulent stream. And her father said: 'You have well done. But I wish it not that my *tantynas*, my joy, should be separated from her love these seven long years. Come, I will send messengers out to find the youth, and whatever journey it may be that he goes upon I will send others in his stead so that he may dwell here and be as a son to me.'

So the King sent messengers out that very hour. And they scoured the kingdom from the high hills of the West to the great plains of the East. But no sign of him could they find, for he had already taken his journey. And the King sent messengers out again to all the kingdoms that bordered upon the land of Powys, but no sign of the lad could those kings find, for he had passed through their lands on his way into a far country whose end is known to no man. So after much searching, the King said to himself: 'I have searched and I have found him not. May it please the gods to keep the boy safe so that my *tantynas*, my Blodwedd, shall not wait in vain.' *Phwlli ap mynath pant bolwyn nach y glasbech –*

'Oh I'm sorry,' said Jackson. 'That's Welsh, of course. I was forgetting that you don't understand.'

Fraser opened his eyes and said: 'It doesn't matter a damn.'

Reader, shall we take this natural break for a bit of swift commentary? The trouble about the Welsh Bardic Tradition – you may have spotted it already – is that it's not particularly hot on précis. Fine, no doubt, for belting it out in the flambeaux-lit halls – not quite so handy when you've got a five-minute spot before the curtain goes up on the main attraction. So without wishing to give too much of a raspberry to the fair Blodwedd, I think we'll sketch in the next half-a-decade or so in a brisk and fairly straight-from-the shoulder style, and then those of us who, unlike Fraser, are still awake can rejoin the main narrative as it grinds to a close. Okay?

Okay.

Briefly, then, what happened was this. Old Maerdrach had been a lifelong sufferer from Prattwinkle's disease, and round about the age of sixty he got a particularly nasty twinge and put the word about that he was going to turn it in. To mark the occasion he dished around among his sons and daughters some pretty ropey-looking presents – a sword, a beer mug, a cow's horn, a tenor banjo – that sort of thing. And, of course, Blodwedd being the youngest didn't qualify for anything better than a small iron box without a key, which on the face of it was pretty bad news as presents go. It was an unexciting box, and as for the contents they were anybody's guess from a cycle-repair outfit to Granny's ashes. However, Maerdrach may have been gaga but he wasn't shtoopid, and he told the fair Blod that if her woodcutter heart-throb didn't put in an appearance she was going to have to shack up with anyone who could answer three rather arch little riddles and open the lid. Blodwedd said, 'Suits me', and, so the King told her the riddles and Blodwedd said, 'You're not serious', and the King said, 'Why, what's wrong with them?', and Blodwedd was just telling him when he suddenly keeled over and died.

Now, when your king died in those days the form was that all the other kings jumped on top of you and tried to hack off a slice of the ancestral lands for themselves. Unsettling perhaps, but then that's how the cookie crumbled. And, frankly, from the other kings' point of view they couldn't have chosen a better time because the sons and daughters of the late Maerdrach hadn't got their act together at all and the upshot was that over the next few years the sons and daughters mostly found themselves being rubbed out. The last to go was the eldest brother who had the rather miffing experience of defeating all his enemies but getting himself so carved up in the process that he couldn't make it back to the château. This left Blodwedd in charge.

Life, as we have just seen, was rough for the ruling classes. But don't let's run away with the idea that the lower orders were rolling around in clover. Far from it. Take for example that young woodcutter laddie. No sooner had he completed his seven-year stretch in foreign parts and set out home to claim the hand of the fabulous Blodwedd than he found himself caught up in the general hostilities and – bingo – he was clapped in the clink of some neighbouring baron, thus failing to put in an appearance at his own wedding. This was hard cheese for Blod, and moreover the iron box idea turned out to be a complete frost. No fewer than four handsome princes turned up at the castle to press their suit, but quite honestly – though they scored well on commitment – it was zero out of ten for riddle-solving, and the end product was that Blodwedd went off and started making table-mats in the East Wing while her lover-boy was about fifty miles down the road tunnelling his way out of durance vile.

That's it folks, so we can now rejoin the mainstream of Jackson's story at the point when the woodcutter finally pops up into the sunlight and hands in his visiting card four or five years too late at the castle lodge:

> Now when the young woodcutter asked to be shewn into the presence of Blodwedd, he was so weary and tattered by his travels, that the porter of the castle would not so much as let him into her sight but went to her himself, and said: 'Your Majesty, there is a ragamuffin fellow at the gate who has come to seek your hand in marriage. Let me now take him the casket so that you may not be troubled by him, and I shall ask him the three questions which your father gave you. Then he may go.' And Blodwedd said: 'Do so.'
>
> So the porter took the casket down to the gate and he placed it in the woodcutter's hands and he asked him the three questions that King Maerdrach had commanded.
>
> And the first question was: What shines brighter than the sun?
>
> And the youth replied: 'The honour of a true man, for that is a light that no curtain can ever hide.'

> And the second question was: What runs faster than the stag?
> And the youth replied: 'The prayers of a true man. For them no hill nor stream can ever stay.'
> And the third question was: What is fairer than the lily flower?
> And the youth replied: 'There is one thing only in this world that is fairer than the lily flower, and that is the hand of Blodwedd, Queen of all the lands of Powys.'
> And as he finished speaking the casket sprang open. And inside upon a bed of satin there lay a ring of the purest gold. And straight away the woodcutter took the ring and carried it up to Blodwedd's chamber and put it upon her finger and kissed her. And she immediately recognised her beloved. And she ordered her chamberlain and her trumpeters to proclaim a feast. And that very evening the two lovers were married amid great celebration. And they ruled together over the land of Powys for many a happy year.

At long last Jackson seemed to have come to a full stop, and I must say the event was greeted by a pretty stunned silence from Henry and Fraser and me. How a man could go around the country – as he obviously did – reciting this twaddle and trying to pass it off as entertainment beats me. Apart from which, the whole thing was as leaky as a sieve. What about the woodcutter's father for a start? Where had he got himself to when all these messengers were flying around taking statements and checking identikits? If he'd only come across with a forwarding address when King Whatsisname was asking people to help the force with their enquiries, he could have saved most of the camp-sites in modern Wales a pretty good slice of wasted time from the likes of Jackson.

Jackson said Wasn't it a lovely thing? And Fraser said Delightful. He said that as he listened to it he had been reminded of an old Scottish ballad which he sometimes liked to recite to discriminating people who were attuned to the nuances of ancient song and story. And Jackson said that that would be lovely but really he must be getting along for his supper. And then Henry put his hand on his shoulder and said No but this was a chance he wouldn't want to miss.

That's the brass neck of a man like Jackson. I suppose that having bored the pants off everybody for the last half-hour or so he imagined he could just slope away and get down to his *boeuf stroganoff* and leave us to take it lying down. Now that he could see some of the solids starting to fly back at him off the fan he didn't like it a bit.

Fraser said, by way of whetting Jackson's appetite so to speak, that this particular ballad called for quite a lot of Scottish dialect which he (Fraser) couldn't really do very well. In fact he could scarcely do it at all, but that wasn't going to prevent him having a good crack at it.

Henry said would Jackson like to know what the ballad was called, and Jackson said Yes, though I must say he sounded low on sincerity.

Fraser said it was called the *Ballad of Sir Patrick Spens*, whereupon quite suddenly Jackson brightened up and announced that he knew it already.

'Oh, *that* old one!' he exclaimed patronisingly. 'Sorry, old boy, but I know it already. Know it pretty well, as a matter of fact.'

'Do you now?' said Fraser. 'Tell me, how does your version go?'

'Well, you know,' Jackson said, 'it goes, let me see … er …

The King sits in Dunfermline town
Drinking the blood-red wine:
'O where'll I find me a skeelie skipper
To sail this new brig o' mine?'

'Then it goes on … um … aha …

Then up and spake a counsellor hoar
Sat at the King's right knee,
Sir …'

'As I thought,' Fraser said. 'The old textbook version. No, the Ballad of Sir Patrick Spens that I'm going to give you is the real thing.'

'That's right,' I said. 'The genuine article. You don't find this sort of thing in print.'

'Too sad, you see,' Henry explained. 'People can't take it.'

Jackson said gloomily, 'Oh, get on.' We'd got him cornered and he knew it.

Fraser then recited in a lingering and plaintive voice his own version of the Ballad of Sir Patrick Spens:

## *Three Men (Not) In a Boat*

The king sits in Dunfermline toun
The Queen sits i' Pitlochrie,
An' the mists an' the rain between the twain
Mak' the A324 a mockrie.

The King sits in Dunfermline toun
And a' his thanes are coming,
Random and rare the laughter there
An' the same goes for the plumbing.

The King sits in Dunfermline toun
Mid his gay but watchful court,
Over mony a year they have learned to fear
The effects of Australian port.

The King sits in Dunfermline toun
Drinking the blude-red wine
'O where'll I find me a skeelie skipper
To sail this new brig o' mine?'

Then up and spak' a counsellor hoar
Wi' a face like a freak October,
'Sir Patrick Spens is the skeeliest skipper
Provided you catch him sober.'

The King has written a broad letter
An' sealed it wi' his hand,
An' sent a man doun the A324
Wi' instructions to hug the land.

The King has written a broad letter
An' sent a man i' the cause,
An' sent him to Sir Patrick Spens
Was walkin' on all fours.

The first word that Sir Patrick read
Sae loud, loud laugh'd he;
The next word that Sir Patrick read
He collapsed in a heap on the quay.

'To Noroway, to Noroway,
To Noroway o'er the faem,
So we'll take a trip to Noroway, lads,
An' be back by opening taem.'

*Putting it Across*

'But it's opening taem already,
An' we're perfectly happy here.'
'Then we'll run on the spot, it'll mak' us hot
And work up a thirst for beer.'

They got him aboard on Thursday,
On Friday they wrang him dry,
On Saturday noon he escaped down the toun
So they had another try.

They finally sailed the next Wednesday
At six o'clock i' the morn,
An' the wave boomed high 'neath a sullen sky
As the mizzen bent i' the storm.

Sir Pat from the bridge looked for'ard
(They had pointed him round that way)
An' the spume flew from his grizzled beard
All the lang, lang day.

Sir Patrick hadna had a drink,
A drink but barely nine,
When he saw three strange shapes
Rising out o' the brine.

Sir Patrick hadna had a drink,
A drink but barely ten,
When he saw three strange shapes
Rising out o' the brine again.

'O bo'sun, bo'sun, I dinna ken
How long ye've been in the navy,
But hae ye ere seen such strange shapes
Risin' out o' the gravy?

'For ane is like my father,
Ane's like my mother dear,
And ane would be like my ain true love
If they'd wean her off the beer.'

'O Captain, tho' the visibility
's particularly murk,
On my aith they be the three grey towers
Of auld Pitlochrie Kirk.

'For this isn't the way to Noroway
An' it isn't the way back hame,
But this is the way up the auld 324
Which is roughly the way we came.'

Now the Queen sat i' Pitlochrie,
An' Sir Patrick he moored by the Grand,
An' he raised himself to his courtly knee
As he kissed her muscular hand.

'O lady, the King has commanded
To bring him a fair young maid,
So by any normal standards
Ye'd be disqualifaid.

'But we live in a time o' crisis
An' ye're goin' to have to do,
So put on your gown, for Dunfermline town
Has been allocated you.'

An' that's how the royals reunited;
The King he threw a ball
For as he explained to the counsellor hoar
'You just can't win 'em all.'

We didn't exchange words after that. Jackson just upped with his stool and went off and skulked in his tent. By the time we'd finished supper he and his wife had put their lamp out and gone to bed. Fraser suggested as we climbed into our sleeping-bags that I should be sent across to sing Cwm Rhondda to him through the canvas, but Henry said he had suffered enough.

Henry seemed to have a gloomy spell generally as we lay awake and talked. He said the air was oppressive, and Fraser said that was a bit rich considering it was his socks that were doing it. Henry complained that we were nearly out of food and he was at his wits' end to think what we could have for breakfast.

I suggested another omelette. 'We can get the eggs from Mrs Evans at the farm,' I said.

Henry said: 'Yes, but it's what we're going to put inside it that's worrying me.'

'Digestive biscuits,' Fraser said. 'We've got some of those left unless you've scoffed them.'

'Apricot jam,' I said.

'Ugh. Just keep quiet for a moment and let me think.'

Five minutes later I said: 'How's the thinking going, Henry?'

But all the answer we got was a loud snore.

# 10

# Kicking it On

We had an odd breakfast next morning. We abandoned the omelette idea, and instead we turned out our hiking bags and divided all the eatables we found into six small courses. Fraser then made Henry write the items down, so that we could have a permanent record.

'You never know,' Fraser said. 'This sort of information could set a whole new trend in menu planning.'

The list read:

Cup of Apricot Jam (each)
Bar of Chocolate or Irish Stew
1 Blood Orange or 5 Sugar Lumps or 2 Digestive Biscuits
Russian Tea
$\frac{1}{4}$ tin of Corned Beef or Lemon Meringue Pie
1 Boiled Sweet

Henry showed signs of panic as he saw the last of our supplies disappearing, but Fraser – who had been talking to some other people on the camp-site (*not* the Jacksons) – told him not to get alarmed. He said apparently there was a town called Knighton about three hours away to the south which actually sat astride the Dyke. We could stock up with groceries there. Speaking for himself, Fraser said, he also intended to find a restaurant or hotel and get himself a four-square lunch while he was on the subject. Henry and I could do as we liked.

It was amazing how this idea about lunch perked us all up.

Before Fraser raised the subject we had been looking on the day ahead as a sort of chore, some dreary uninviting task which had to be trundled through for the next eight or ten hours before the great *concierge* in the sky came round and said 'Lights out', when we could all get back into bed and go to sleep again. Now we couldn't spring along fast enough.

It's an interesting thing about walking – and I suppose it's true about life as well – that provided you're aiming at some sort of target you seen to have a great deal of incidental fun along the way. But take that target away and the whole thing becomes as blank and featureless as a swamp. That's why, speaking for myself, I could never take up jogging. You're not going anywhere. I should explain for the benefit of those readers who may skim through this book in two or three hundred years' time and wonder what the hell I am talking about, that jogging is the latest in that long series of fashions that the civilised world has devised to prove to itself that meaningless tedium carries an extra-special virtue of its own. Every century has its peculiar form of disease. In the seventeenth century it was listening to sermons, in the nineteenth governing Australia. Now it's jogging. Anyone – so the argument goes – anyone who can do anything so pointless and monotonous as that has *got* to be someone we can be proud of. And of course if you were to do an in-depth study of the thing, and research its history, you would find that all the spadework for the movement, all the getting it off the ground so to speak, was probably done generations ago by a whole string of super-bores who make the mere modish trendy of today seem practically effervescent by comparison. Karl Marx was a secret jogger. So was Matthew Arnold. Then of course you got D.H. Lawrence and Mahatma Gandhi and that lot. And before you know where you are they're offering degree courses in the subject along with Social Studies and Applied Vandalism.

I only went jogging once and that was by mistake. It was when I had been in London a few months and I found myself sharing a flat with another newcomer to the city who was joining our firm on the same day. I should explain that this was in the late sixties, quite a few years before people were used to seeing joggers in this country; but my flat-mate had just completed a Business Management course in America where jogging was one of the principal skills they taught you, and I think he had some sort of missionary fervour about converting the United Kingdom.

My friend had learned something else at Business School which – looking back – I suppose was the prime cause of the near riot we created when we set out on our jog. He had learned to talk in a weird unearthly accent, which made about one quarter of everything he said quite incomprehensible. When I had got to know him better he explained to me one day that this method of speech was essential to his profession. He said that Americans were able to understand the accent no better than Englishmen, but anybody who couldn't make the noise in the Business Management world stood no chance of rising to the top of the tree. He said that if he didn't talk like that he would be ostracised by his colleagues and sent off to do studies on matchbox vendors in Worksop.

'I suppose we'd better catch a tube in the morning,' I said to him on the Sunday night before we signed on.

'Uhuh,' he replied, shaking his head – by which I understood him to mean No. 'The – aw – arptimum route T is – aw – matrafact the – aw – No. 8 bus out of Saint Jan's Wood which gives us a drarparff rightaround the – aw – Mansion House. Weidenwe take that?'

I said: 'Fine.' (I'm sorry, incidentally, that the ordinary common-or-garden alphabet can't really do justice to the language of Business Managementese – but I hope you get the general drift of the thing.)

I said: 'What time shall we set out?'

'Eight aclerk,' he said.

So we went to bed.

Now my friend had said eight o'clock – at least he *said* he'd said eight o'clock, but for some reason or other what I heard him say was a quarter past seven. We tried later on to reconstruct the two sounds to see if there was any way we could get them confused for each other again, but we never came to any firm conclusion. Our landlord complained that the experiment was upsetting the other residents of the house and we must either talk normally or get out.

Anyway, when I appeared from my room at about 7.14 and 30 seconds, allowing the usual half-minute for breakfast, I found him already going out of the front door.

'If yore calming you'd bedder calm, T,' he said. So I grabbed up my briefcase and ran down the steps with him into the street. We turned left and jogged along the kerb towards the traffic lights. There was nobody much about, but the man who had the paper shop four doors down leaped backwards with a start as we ran by and put his foot in the bucket he had been using to wash down the pavement, and two kids who had been playing about near the railings picked up their football and ran after us as though somebody had just told them where they could find a hidden cache of Mars bars.

'Wotz this then?' said one kid as they scampered along.

'It's yer Olympic afletes, innit,' said the other knowledgeably. 'This one 'ere's the aflete, see. An' the uvver one's 'is lawyer wot's guardin' his amateur status and collectin' all the bribes.'

The four of us ran on together for a little way. Then when we got half-way along the next street a small border collie suddenly ran out at us through an open garden gate, and he joined in the race with his master after him in hot pursuit; and then a witless youth who had been repairing his motor-bike by the side of the road suddenly threw down his spanner and started pounding along behind. Over the next half-mile or so our numbers swelled into double figures. Two housewives who had been abusing each other in a routine sort of way on the corner of a little square cast aside their antagonisms and attached themselves to the crowd.

'Do you think it's really him, dear?' one of them kept saying to the other.

'Of course its 'im,' the other said. 'Recognise 'im anywhere, I would. 'E's late for the studio, that's why 'e's running.'

We picked up three or four more at the Cumbernauld Arms, where a group of brewer's men were tossing barrels down on to the pavement; and the pedestrian crossing on Queen's Grove doubled our numbers again at a single stroke. By the time we got on to the main thoroughfare at Wellington Road there must have been a good twenty-five people in the chase, and the policeman on duty outside Lords held the traffic up specially to let us through.

All this time, of course, I had supposed that we were running for a bus. I had been so preoccupied with keeping abreast of my flat-mate that it hadn't occurred to me to look him over and see whether he was dressed for the City as I was. By the time we began the downhill gallop from Lord's Cricket Ground to Maida

Vale, however, his superior stamina was beginning to tell, and with a quick spurt he ran ahead and came full into view. I have always maintained, and I still do, that it was the sight of him in a lilac-coloured tracksuit and *not* the fact that I was weakened from exhaustion that caused me to veer suddenly from my direct path and crash into a lamp-post, thus bringing the whole expedition to a halt.

The policeman came running up and demanded to know what was going on. He received an alarming variety of replies. One woman insisted that we had all been running down to Queensway for the start of the summer sales.

'Give over, duckie!' cried a tall man in a waistcoat. 'We're chasing this dog here. It's a Cruft's Champion, see. You've only got to look at the hindquarters to tell it's got class.'

A third said it was something to do with Nuclear Disarmament, and the two housewives insisted that my flat-mate was Sean Connery and I was his keep-fit adviser.

They asked my flat-mate, but either they couldn't understand him or they simply didn't believe what he said. I suppose the idea that somebody could create a major incident by the simple expedient of jogging from nowhere to nowhere seemed too fanciful to be taken seriously.

In the end they all switched their attention to me. They sat me up against the lamp-post and slapped my face to make sure I was awake, and then they knelt down and peered at me and the policeman asked me what we'd been doing. I looked at him, and I looked at all the faces, and I looked at my friend who was still gesticulating wildly in a lilac-coloured sort of way, and I gave them the only answer I could.

'I haven't the least idea,' I said.

I think if the policemen hadn't been there the crowd would have lynched us. They surged around muttering menacingly, and a woman who had been calling out for some minutes that I was a Russian defector making a dash for freedom suddenly changed her tune and said that people like me ought to be pulled out of society and kept behind bars.

It took the policeman about five minutes to get the crowd to go away, and when he had us alone he took down our names and addresses and gave us an official caution. He said that no proceedings would be taken against us this time, but if we got ourselves into trouble again we'd have the full majesty of the law to contend with.

I took his advice, and I have never been jogging since. It seems to me that if the people who indulge in these hazardous sports would only stop and think of the trouble it causes everyone else when they get into difficulties, they'd give them up straight away and settle for something less risky, like hang-gliding.

I had a tune running through my head as we walked along, so I fell behind and whistled it quietly to myself – you know what a bad ear for music Fraser and Henry have. It was the one which goes tum-te-tum-tum tum-te-tum-tum tum-tum-tum-tum tum-te-tum-tum – I expect you probably know it. I whistled it for several reasons. First of all it was there – tunes have a habit of coming into your head when you're walking, don't they? In the second place it was a lovely day with a clear sky and a cool breeze, and it all seemed to fit in. And thirdly, when we were just about half-way through our morning's stint I suddenly had a thought which started to worry me to begin with, but after a bit it seemed to be rather funny, so I thought I would keep it to myself until the right moment came. Then I would spring it on the other two and watch them beginning to panic. That made me whistle all the better.

Henry and Fraser had started off trying to tackle some sort of brain-teaser – the sort of thing I imagine they set you in intelligence tests. A man wakes up in the middle of the night and hears the Town Hall clock strike two. Now, he knows that the clock strikes the correct number of clangs on each hour, and it strikes once at quarter-past, and twice at half-past, and once again at a quarter-to. How long will it be before he knows for certain what the time is? Or something like that. The answer, of course, which you're never allowed to give for some reason, is just as long as it takes him to pick up the telephone and dial the speaking clock. They argued so long, Henry and Fraser, that I was half expecting it to turn into a punch-up, but then when I listened to them again a mile or so further on they had got on to another subject, namely lunch, drink, and stocking up with food. And a few minutes later we came over the top of a hill called Panpunton Hill and there was the little town of Knighton lying beneath us in the valley.

Fraser and Henry sat down on a rock and started congratulating themselves. 'There she is,' they said to each other. 'Now, the time is just coming up to 1.30, so we'll be there by two. We can have a drink for half an hour and then go out and find something to eat.'

I decided to unleash my surprise. 'You're overlooking one thing,' I said.

'What's that?' they said.

I said, 'Today's Sunday. Closing time'll be two o'clock, and you won't find a café open for love nor money.'

I don't know when I've seen two expressions change so fast. One minute they were swathed in complacent smiles, the next they were all anger and savagery and accusation. 'What the devil are you grinning about?' they shouted at me. And, 'Don't just stand there smirking – get a move on.' And more terrible stuff which I would blush to relate. Most of it, I'm glad to say, was more or less hurled backwards at me as they pounded down the hill, and what with the banging of their boots and the wide range of vocabulary I couldn't do much more than grasp the general meaning. Anyway, since I'd had plenty of time to adjust to the idea that we were going to be late, I was happy just to stroll downhill at an easy amble, keeping my eye on them as they hurried between the first houses and a moment later emerged to view in the High Street and dived into the Swan Hotel.

As it happened I was wrong. Sunday closing in Knighton is a good solid sensible 2.30. So Henry and Fraser had forty-five minutes drinking time, and I had half an hour. Then, by prior arrangement with the landlord, we went into the dining room and sat down to a late lunch.

There was one other party in the dining room of the Swan Hotel, but it was a large party of, I think, ten people. Nine of these were looking dismal and uneasy and boxed in. The tenth was looking extraordinarily authoritative and pleased with himself.

'This is a surprisingly good claret,' he was saying loudly to the waiter as we came through the door. 'Really quite a robust little wine. Good afternoon,' he said, raising his glass to us when we advanced into the room. 'Your very good health, gentlemen.'

I said, 'Good afternoon, Doctor.'

And Fraser said, 'Good health, Doctor.'

And Henry said, 'Cheers.'

Then we sat down at our table and turned our backs on him.

It silenced him – this calling him 'Doctor', I mean. Of course, he *was* a doctor, but – although I couldn't see his face – I could sort of feel him wondering to himself how we had worked it out. The fact is of course, that we didn't know for sure. We were just relying on the proven fact that about ninety-five per cent of all the people who can be found wrecking otherwise enjoyable meals these days by banging on about wine are in point of fact G.P.s, heart surgeons, consultant neurologists and others of that kidney. In the narrow circles in which they move a knowledge of wine passes for culture. That is why they are always trying to convince everybody else that they've got it.

Let me explain a little more. A doctor's training is a hard one. He normally starts at the age of about 17, and after a four-year gap playing Rugby for the Harlequins, he finishes up being let loose on the patients somewhere between 45 and 50 when they've run out of any further exams that they can set him. All this time he is studying for papers, learning the difference between tennis elbow and beri-beri – that sort of thing. Then suddenly, when he is about half-way through the course and starting to get middle-aged, he wakes up one morning and realises that there is a whole world of enlightenment and artistic endeavour outside the walls of the hospital about which he knows absolutely nothing. It is at this point that he becomes a potential nuisance.

Now I have it on good medical authority that all doctors go through this period of self-realisation. The nice lazy ones, of course – the ones who finish up prescribing a pint of Guinness twice a day – soon learn to live with their lack of breadth; they do nothing at all about the deficiency, and spend the rest of their lives on perfectly good terms with everybody, even the surviving relatives of their patients.

The others, however, are different. They are the ones who hurl aside their black mood with a cry of impatience and decide to do something about it. Naturally, being men of science, they then fall into the trap of thinking that the problem can be resolved by some sort of self-set examination, and they cast around for a subject which can be mugged up quick and – more important – regurgitated ever afterwards to impress their few remaining friends. Wine fills the bill ideally. After all, when you think about it, the stuff comes in just three colours – red, white, and pink – and the important areas that grow it can't number more than thirty or so. Put these together and mix in a few other ingredients like the quality of the soil and the character of the grape and you are well on your way to becoming an expert. What's more, if you get into difficulties you've always got the label – and of course the price – to tell you how much you are supposed to be enjoying it.

The final touch comes with the use of the right phrases, and this is generally picked up by hanging around other doctors with the same complaint and listening to how they do it. You don't say, 'This wine is red and produces much the same effect as methylated spirits at about forty times the price.' You say, 'This is *surprisingly* good. Really *quite robust*. A *nice little* wine.' And of course, '*Living up to the promise of its nose*.' You have to be patronising to the wine, you see, to give everybody the impression that back home you are drinking Château Grotheimer '47 at a hundred and twenty pounds a bottle.

I think we saved the meal for that party by calling the man 'Doctor'. It flung him into a mood of contemplation, and all the rest of them correspondingly cheered up. He tried once or twice to stage a comeback and asked them if they knew anything about the grape-harvesting techniques in Alsace. One of the men said he did, and then he told a rather risqué and quite irrelevant story about a chambermaid and a cider press which made all the girls laugh. After that there was no stopping them, and by the time we left the wine expert had pulled away from the rest of the party and was sitting morosely by himself, sniffing a cork.

On the far edge of Knighton we found a Sunday shop open. We stocked up with provisions and then set out walking towards Kington.

It must be very confusing having two towns called Knighton and Kington just ten miles apart. The main difference between them is that Knighton is in Wales and is also on the Dyke. Kington is a mile or so on the English side of the border, and, with typically English reserve, it has stepped aside from the Dyke and allowed the earthwork to go harmlessly past.

We weren't very much excited by the idea of Kington, I don't know why. Somehow it seemed rather spineless to have come all this way and then be spending the night on the English side of the border. So, when we had walked the hilly miles past Presteigne and round the slopes of an enormous Iron Age camp which Offa had taken one look at and decided to dodge past, we turned off along the road to Old Radnor just to be sure that we remained in Wales. And, as good luck would have it, about the hour of the evening pint, a roadside boozer hove into view bearing the good honest sign of The Plough above its door. And, to cut a long story short, while we were ruminating on his excellent ale, we negotiated with the landlord for a night's lodging. And he took us into the barn and made room for us by moving over the old ram which was tethered there; and by the time we came back inside for an egg and chips we were washed and brushed, with our sleeping-bags spread out on the straw and our hearts ready to receive the burst of Welsh song which began to well up around the crowded bar an hour or two later.

The singing from that bar I shall never forget. Singing is the great glory of the Welsh. I am told that in all Europe only two nations can come close to them for their in-dyed sense of song. These are the Poles and the Basques. But I shall not travel to either of these countries only to be disappointed by the comparison with Wales. No finer sound can rise spontaneously from the throats of men than rose from The Plough that evening – so why should I cross continents to learn what I know already?

Englishmen can sometimes be very silly about Welsh music, and it arises I supposes from an inferiority complex. They know that they haven't got the passion and the bravura to do the job themselves, and so they look around for some way of damning the superior article with faint praise.

An Englishman once told me a story – a shaggy second-hand story, if ever I heard one – to illustrate what he said were the limitations of Welsh music.

An Englishman applied to a large Welsh chapel for the job of professional organist and choirmaster. At the appointed time he presented himself before the assembled elders to be interviewed.

'Tell me, boy,' said the senior elder. 'You are supposed to be bloody hot at music, see. What do you think of Beethoven now?'

'Beethoven?' said the organist cheerfully. 'I know him quite well, as a matter of fact. Beethoven happens to be my brother-in-law.'

'Does he now? Well, what about Mozart then, tell me that?'

'Since you mention it,' said the organist, 'I know Mozart pretty closely as well. Mozart, you know, was a great friend of my father's for years and years.'

'I see. And Benjamin Britten, boy. Do you know him too?'

'Oh yes,' said the organist. 'I was at school with Benjamin Britten. Now if you don't mind I think I'd better be getting along. I've got to catch the 4.15 from Cardiff back to London.'

After the Englishman had left all the elders put their heads together to consider their verdict.

'I wouldn't bother with him, if you take my advice,' pronounced the senior elder as they sat around. 'He's a bloody liar for the start, see. I know for a fact because my brother works on the railway: there's no such train as the 4.15 to London.'

What a dismal and appalling story! Without a seed of truth – which is what every story has to have if it is going to strike any sort of chord in the listener. Can't you just hear the gasping and croaking that would come up from the larynx of the man who told me *that*, if you presented him with a sheet of music and asked him to sing a single line. When your musical performance is one twentieth as good as that of a Welsh petrol-pump attendant, my friend, then I'll bother with you. In the mean time get back to your Kensington flat and listen to Mahler on the stereo.

We went to sleep with 'Land of My Fathers' ringing in our ears.

# 11

# Tracking it Down

Monday morning 7th June: Rain. Henry snoring unpleasantly.

I write these few words in diary form, because on this particular morning I had diaries on the brain. I discovered, you see, that I was not the only member of the party who was planning to put pen to paper about our trip to Offa's Dyke. Henry, it appeared, was keeping a notebook, and of all the stupid, self-satisfied, inaccurate entries ever to greet a man's eyes as he emerges from the sleeping-bag. – But not too fast.

What happened was this. Henry was still pottering about the barn when I went to sleep the night before. I suppose he did this deliberately, waiting for me to drop off before he picked up his pencil and started scribbling by the light of his torch. Then, when he had finished, he probably tucked the diary under his sleeping-bag and promptly proceeded to turn and grunt and toss around so much for the rest of the night that it eventually worked free and was just sitting there wide open for me to read it when I woke up.

It said:

6th June. Sunday. Fine weather.

Then if you please, he launched straight in with:

Am getting worried about T. Beginning to show signs of cracking

> up. Fell behind all morning and couldn't maintain the pace. Keeps whistling in high-pitched demented way, always same erratic notes without variation. At mid-day made wild false statements about local pub closing-times. Limped into Swan Hotel very late and looking pale, but managed to slightly improve in p.m. Must watch him closely. Lacks the sheer grit and muscle for this sort of ordeal.

Huh!

I saw that Fraser was awake and I read the extract over to him. Fraser riled me by saying he thought it was unexceptional. He said the only comment he had was that 'to slightly improve' was a split infinitive, but then one couldn't really expect style from a statistician. So then I turned back in the book and found a passage about Fraser opening the tin of sardines. That made him sit up with a jolt.

'But ... you ... what ... He can't put down that sort of stuff!' Fraser exclaimed scrambling out of bed and then finding out how cold it was and scrambling back in again. 'That just isn't true!'

'Oh, I don't know,' I said casually. 'I suppose one *could* describe your tin-opening ideas as "daft as a chicken" and "doomed to disaster from the word go". Rather telling phrases as a matter of fact.'

We looked at each other. We were both on the same wave-length.

We got up quietly and dressed, and buried our knapsacks in the straw. Then we grabbed hold of the ram's halter and passed the end of it through the bolt-socket on the doorpost and hauled the animal in on the line till it completely blocked the only way to the yard outside. Then I wrote Henry a charming little note which I put beside his pillow, while Fraser reached Henry's watch down from its nail and moved the hands round to eleven o'clock. And after all *that* we tiptoed up the ladder to the loft and lay there above his head dropping straw down on him until he woke up.

It takes quite a lot of straw to wake Henry up, so by the time he opened his eyes he was fairly covered in it. He lay there for a while wiggling his eyebrows and trying to blow it off his nose. Then he sat up and looked round.

'Hey!' we heard him mutter to himself when he saw the barn was empty. 'Hey! You lot!'

There was a pause, then 'Wazzatime?' as he suddenly sprang out of bed and looked at his watch. '11.15. Hell – they haven't gone, have they? They can't have gone without me.'

'Wazzat?' – he has put his foot on my note now, and he picks it up and starts mouthing it over to himself in great gulps of anguish. 'Couldn't wake you ... thought we'd let you sleep on ... meet you in Kington at twelve o'clock. Oh you bastards! It's nearly half-past eleven now. I haven't a hope in hell of getting to Kington by ... Now, now,' he tells himself. 'Steady down and get moving. Shirt – ah here. Pants. Trousers.' He goes through the whole of his laundry list as he puts them on. He seems to find it comforting. Then, when he is finally all strapped up, he sets off down the barn and comes straight up against the ram.

'H ... Hallo,' says Henry to the ram, jerking to an abrupt halt and looking round as though somebody is going to help him. 'Hallo, hallo, hallo. H ... How did you get here then, old lad.'

He considers the problem, and he decides to try coaxing the ram over to one side of the door frame while he edges past on the other. 'Now then, you come over here, there's a good ... wooah!' The ram gives a violent lurch towards him and pulls up short on the outstretched halter.

'Now I suppose,' said Henry, clinging apprehensively to the wall, 'if I got this old piece of corrugated iron and sort of pre ... ssed you back gently I could ...'

Be-bom, Clang! The ram seems to be in an argumentative mood this morning. Indifferent to the chances of getting a headache itself, it hurtles against the tin and bowls Henry to the ground. Henry slithers away from danger without getting up, and lying back on the straw peers out into the yard through a knothole in the boarded wall.

'Help,' he says feebly. The only response is from a nearby hen which, by the sound of it, lays an egg on the other side of the wall and starts cackling around the yard telling everybody about it.

Henry puts out a listless arm across the straw, and feels something bulky, and after fumbling cautiously around for a minute or two he uncovers Fraser's knapsack. 'The stupid clown's left this behind,' he mutters to himself. 'What a fool.' Then he finds mine, and we can practically hear him trying to work it all out.

At this point my knee suddenly crashes through the rotten

floorboards of the loft and the game is up.

Henry is all wounded pride and bad language as we clamber down the ladder. He can't pretend he wasn't taken in – he knows Fraser and I have heard too much for that. In fact there is so much pent-up emotion in the air that we all saddle ourselves up and start off across the yard without even remembering to have breakfast.

'I think you've forgotten this,' I said to Henry as we turned out on to the road, and I handed him his notebook. He sort of breathed it into his clothing like a card-sharper palming an ace.

'Those are my bird-watching notes,' he said a minute later when he had had time to work out an excuse. But he didn't fool anybody.

About four miles beyond Kington the sun came out, and at the same time Offa's Dyke came to an abrupt halt.

Again.

There was a man standing on the bank at the end who seemed to be very knowledgable. An archaelogist most likely.

'That's right,' he said when we pointed out that the Dyke had gone missing. 'It's eight or nine miles on to the next stretch and that runs from Mansell Gamage to Bridge Sollers. Look, you can see Mansell Copse down there in the valley. In the eighth century the woods grew so thick along the Wye that there was no way through for an invading army, so that meant there was no need for dyke building.'

The man may have been right or he may have been wrong, but at least he sounded as though he knew what he was talking about. I pointed this out to Fraser as we made our way down to the valley floor, but Fraser said I shouldn't get carried away by it. 'Sounding convincing is the stock-in-trade of those lads,' he said. 'It's part of their training. Same thing with economists. If they can't make it sound convincing nobody's going to bother listening to them at all. The woollier the subject,' Fraser said, 'the more authoritative the so-called expert.'

Fraser said that on a good day, when it came to thinking on your feet, an archaeologist in form ought to be able to leave an economist or a politician standing. He'd seen an example of it during his last year at school when he did some work on an enormous Stone Age site in Dorset which was being excavated by

Sir Mortimer Wheeler. Fraser said he'd never forgotten it.

Henry said: 'Your memory goes back a long way.'

And Fraser said: 'No. Sir Mortimer lived to a great age.'

Fraser said that the digging work on the site was done in layers, with every foot of depth representing a hundred years or so of history. You'd only got to find something on the top and let it slip through your fingers, and it would be picked up by the gang down below and attributed to the wrong millennium. This seemed to happen quite often, and in fact Fraser noticed after a while that all the old hands kept to the high ground where they could chuck things over the edge if they didn't fancy the trudge back to the site office to report the find.

Anyway, in the midst of all this confusion, Fraser found a hole. It was about ten feet across, and the mud inside it was paler and crumblier than the mud outside it – that's how they knew it had been a hole in the first place. It wasn't just a shallow hole either, but it went down and along for forty or fifty feet like a burrow.

Fraser's hole caused quite a bit of consternation. His site leader didn't know what it was, and he went and called the site supervisor. The site supervisor said he didn't know what it was either, and he got the area controller out of the office to come and look at it. The area controller was a tall pimply man with glasses and he nearly fell over with emotion at the sight of Fraser's hole, but he didn't have any more idea about what it was than any of the others.

In the end the momentous decision was taken to summon Sir Mortimer Wheeler from a completely different part of the dig to tell them what it could be. Sir Mortimer, being a very experienced hand indeed and a master of timing, did absolutely nothing at all for the next hour and a half, so that by the time his Land Rover cruised into view across the earthworks the party round Fraser's hole was near to collapse from nervous exhaustion and excitement.

'Ah yes,' Sir Mortimer announced in his grandest manner as he inspected the object of everyone's attention. 'No problems there, Blathering. That's nothing more nor less than an early flint-mine. Dug by the Stone Age inhabitants to provide themselves with implements.' And so saying he turned stylishly on his heel and started ambling back towards the car.

There was a breathless, emphatic silence.

'B ... but, Sir Mortimer!' exclaimed the area controller, suddenly pulling himself together and running after the archaeologist almost triumphantly. 'Sir Mortimer. You say it's a Stone Age flint mine. B ... but Sir! There isn't any flint within twenty miles of this spot!'

Sir Mortimer gave Blathering a wan smile as he settled himself down in his seat. 'Of course there isn't, dear boy,' he said. 'Of course there isn't. But *they* weren't to know that, were they?'

Nice one, Mort. That's the sort of fast thinking that gets you the job.

The valley of the Wye has been completely spoiled for later generations by the diaries of the Reverend Francis Kilvert, who was curate of Clyro some two miles from Hay from 1865 to 1872. Kilvert, a noted jogger – and, believe it or not, a grown man – was capable of writing such things as:

> Sunday 14th April
>
> The beauty of the view, the first view of the village, coming down by the Brooms this evening was indescribable. The brilliant golden poplar spires shone in the evening light like flames against the dark hillside of the Old Forest and the blossoming fruit trees, the torch trees of Paradise, blazed with a transparent green and white lustre up the dingle in the setting sunlight. The village is in a blaze of fruit blossom. Clyro at its loveliest. What more can be said?

Several acres more, unfortunately. Not that I blame Kilvert. A man can write what he likes in a diary unless – like Henry's – the thing is a blatant distortion. No, and you can't really blame his widow either. She did her best, poor dear – burned as much of the stuff as she could. But either a couple of wardrobes-full managed to slip her notice, or, more likely, she just didn't have the modern incinerating equipment which you need to tackle this size of assignment. Anyway the upshot is that the whole valley is dotted through these days with Kilvert buffs gasping and wondering and generally holding up the flow of traffic.

We saw this quite literally at first hand when we got down to the A 4112 early in the afternoon. The traffic on the main road was down to a crawl, and as we strode into the next village we saw the reason for it, namely that a Country Fayre was in progress. You notice that I spell 'Country Fayre' in the Elizabethan way to distinguish it from the proper old fashioned style of the thing with honest amusements like Bowling for a Pig and Guessing the Weight of the Vicar.

This was the modern version. Round Tablers, Skydivers, Traction Engine Rallies, Town Crier Competitions, Real Ale Tents, and – for no Country Fayre can ever be completely bogus without it – the Dancing of the Morris. Morris Dancing (I say this for the benefit of my numberless foreign readers) is a practice of seeming antiquity which in fact was invented towards the end of the last century by a man with the unlikely name of C. Sharp. In it some sixteen or twenty men – large ones usually with black beards – are required to leap around with string tied below the knee to the accompaniment of a concertina. Then they all drink pints of beer and reassure their audience that there will be more of the same horrendous material later on.

Now, I'm not saying that Kilvert Buffs and Morris Men are the same thing. Of course not. Kilvert Buffs don't usually carry concertinas for a start; and as for a Morris Man, he would probably have to have had several pints too many before you found him lurching along a hedgerow looking for voles. What I do say is that the two types blend into each other, and what is worse they tend to blend across important main roads like the A 4112, just when all the right-thinking members of the population are trying to get to a race-meeting.

What is needed on these occasions, I always think, is some form of extra support for the police. The single rozzer, with his magenta face and blue uniform beneath the pitiless sun, is an admirable sight as he allows first a Kentish hop-dance, next two Belgian juggernauts and a removal van to pass along the narrow High Street. But I couldn't help wondering as I watched the timeless gyrations of the quaintly-clad dancing figures whether the moment hadn't come to shunt them off to a disused railway siding somewhere to carry on their folklore experiments in relative seclusion.

I needn't have worried. Help was at hand. The dog Woofera had obviously got this stretched of Dykeland pretty well sussed out. You can imagine the scene. Far back in his mountain HQ, where a paw-picked team of planner-dogs are putting their final touches to the scheme for general revolution, word comes in from the field that the Morris Dancers are staging a show of force at Little Ditteridge in the Neap. Around the darkened walls of the cave a score of battle-hardened muzzles crack open into grins of disbelief. This one is going to be easy.

The team is picked, the orders are given – brief, barked commands, no fancy stuff needed for these veterans. Then comes the swoop down the hill, the quick rendezvous with the local unit, and half an hour later a thin line of curly tails can be seen making its way along the back lane into the village. Once they get to the High Street they split up. Most of them slouch indolently down by ones and twos towards the Dancers, while the hit squad work over a small child behind an ice-cream van and run off along the back streets with his balloon, leaving him grizzling. Just as the dance is reaching its climax the hit squad bound back into the High Street out of an alleyway and start doing a balloon dance of their own in amongst the Morris Men's feet. Now the others join in. Professional, efficient, not a movement wasted, they've got five of the Morris Men down before the front end of the dance has even noticed what is happening. Those who are still dancing start treading on the fingers of those who are getting up, and cries of rage are punctuated from time to time by the fresh thump of falling bodies. Then Che Woofera takes a mouthful out of the concertina and the whole performance wheezes to a stop.

The policeman, who has been talking to an anxious motorist, now turns round and decides that it is time to call a halt. The dogs all stroll off into shop doorways and sit there impassively watching the Morris Dancers packing up their equipment.

Che comes up to me and offers me a slice of concertina. 'Have it, if you like,' he says. 'It's up to you. I've got plenty of this sort of thing back at base, so I'll be leaving it here in any case.'

Che decided to walk on with us to Mansell Gamage and the Dyke. 'I might as well,' he said. 'There are a couple of things I've got to check out down there in any case. It's not often I find the time to get this far south.'

Mansell Gamage was a pleasant little place. It was also quite a peaceful little place until we arrived at about four o'clock in the afternoon. As we turned into the main street we found a youngish but distinctly hard-muscled lady trying to reverse a horsebox into a gateway.

Fraser volunteered his help.

'How frightfully nice of you,' she screamed.

Fraser and Che Woofera walked round the car and weighed the situation up.

'No problems there,' said Che.

'None at all,' said Fraser.

'Sure you don't want my help?' said Che. 'Well, in that case I'll leave it to you.'

While this short exchange had been going on between Fraser and the dog, the lady had started the car up and Fraser made her bring it forward a few yards on to the edge of the road.

'Stop!' he said, when he'd got her into the right starting position. 'Now then, left hand down and into reverse. Right – back you come. Come on, back you come. More. More.'

'I'm not going to hit the wall, am I?' said the lady.

'You're not,' said Fraser, 'because I'm going to stop you before you do.'

'Okay.'

'You've got a couple of yards yet. Back. Back. Bac ... ck. What the hell's that dog doing?' said Fraser suddenly.

'Where?' I said from across the street.

'There in that garden. It's starting to dig its way into a chicken run.'

'Which garden?'

'That garden.'

'Oh yes. But that isn't our dog.'

'Yes it is.'

'No it's not. Henry,' I said, 'take a look at that dog. It doesn't look a bit like ours, does it?'

'Dunno,' said Henry with all the commitment of the true bystander. 'Could be. On the other hand, possibly not.'

'Grief!' exclaimed Fraser looking skywards for support. 'We've got a couple of lunatics here! We've only been walking with the thing for the last two hours, not to mention the greater part of the last week, and you stand there and say that it isn't the same dog. Look, I was talking to it a moment ago. Any fool can see that it's ...'

*Crash*!

'Stop!' said Fraser to the muscular lady as she leaped out of the car to inspect the damage.

'I'm going to get my husband,' she said in a voice which had risen by an augmented fifth since we heard it last.

The three of us stood still and waited. It was quite a long wait, and that made us uncomfortable.

Now, I must admit the lady hadn't said what her husband was like. She'd just said that she was going to get him. But, on the other hand, when a woman who looks as though she's training for the Modern Pentathlon herself goes to get succour from her mate, one has reason to expect the worst. One imagines him, does one not, as well-built and powerful. Swarthy too, I shouldn't wonder – the sort of man who may be tearing up telephone directories indoors and won't take kindly to being disturbed.

When he appeared we thought it was some sort of joke. We thought the real husband was going to come vaulting over the wall the next moment and startle us into settling his insurance claim.

The man was small and pale, and by the look of him he collected butterflies. He said, 'Oh dear, oh dear.' Then, when he caught sight of the three of us – and, come to think of it, we were no sight for the faint-hearted after a week in the hills – he sort of shied away and took up a defensive position at the corner of the horsebox.

Fraser said he was sorry, terribly sorry; and the man said, 'Oh, thank you.' And the lady said that what her husband wanted to know was what were we going to do about it. And the man said, Yes – that's what he wanted to know. And Fraser said he was going to offer him his sincere apologies. And the lady said that her husband didn't think that was good enough. And the man said, Quite, he rather wondered whether that was good enough. And Fraser said had he got any better ideas. And the lady said her husband had got lots of ideas: he wasn't a man to be fobbed off. And the man said up to a point that was true.

Fortunately at that moment the horse, which up to now had remained off-stage chewing the cud, suddenly took it into its head to play the scene for laughs. It stuck its face out of the back of the horsebox and, grinning toothily, started to do a tap-dance inside with its back feet. This diverted the lady's attention, and she became preoccupied with browbands and bridles and the like.

We bowed deeply and took a hasty leave. On the way past the neighbouring garden we collected the dog Woofera – needless to say it *had* been Woofera that had been tunnelling into that chicken-run. The householder ran out and abused us, but we told him that he ought to be thankful to have fallow ground so throughly dug over. So we continued our charitable way out of the village and up the wooded slopes of Mansell Hill to make contact with Offa's Dyke once more.

Contact we made, and we followed the Dyke along, and it came down the far end of Mansell Hill and across a field and up to a main road and then it fizzled out. Marvellous piece of work this stretch – every bit of two miles long. Just the job for keeping out ten thousand Welshmen, provided you can persuade them to aim straight for it.

Then I sprained my ankle. I wasn't even walking. I just put one foot backwards to steady myself and stepped straight into a rabbit hole.

We got my boot off and we got my sock off, and we all had a good look at it to see how the swelling was coming along. Che Woofera put his nose up against it in a sympathetic sort of way and Fraser gave it a squeeze and said it looked as if it could be serious.

'Pretty bad, do you think?' said Che.

''Fraid so,' said Fraser.

'Broken probably?'

'I should say so.'

'Well, there you are,' said Che. 'If you'd only consulted me instead of barging about all over the place this accident needn't have happened at all. It's a dangerous little thing is a rabbit hole. I had an aunt who got stuck in one once. We couldn't get her in or out, and after she'd been there a couple of days we had to make a deal with the inhabitants. A team of rabbits pushing at one end, and a team of dogs pulling her tail at the other. Remind me to tell you the story some time. Now, let me see, have we got a clean break?'

'Hard to tell,' said Henry.

'Patient seems dazed.'

Yes. That's congenital.'

(You notice the way they consult the stretcher-case, these medical experts.)

They got me to my feet.

'Right my lad,' Henry said. 'We'll have to get you out of here.'

'I would have thought that was pretty obvious,' I said with a wince. But I said it nicely, if you know what I mean. It doesn't pay to antagonise the male nurses when you're wounded on the front line.

So we hobbled to the roadside fence, and politely declining a lift over, I crawled through beneath the bottom rail with Che Woofera going ahead to show me how to do it. And from there they dragged me the last twelve feet or so to the edge of the tarmac.

# 12

# Packing it In

Frankly we hitched a lift.

I told the other two not to bother about me. I said that if they propped me up against the side of the road I could thumb down a lorry as well as the next man. I said that in all probability they had only to walk another thirty miles or so before they came to the next stretch of Dyke and I didn't want to spoil their enjoyment.

Fraser and Henry said No. They said there was nothing they would have liked better than another thirty miles, but they didn't intend to let a pal down. They said the right place for me was in hospital. I said I had no intention of going to hospital, but I wouldn't say no to a three-star hotel and a decent meal and a bath. And they said they could just about endure that, if I felt it was absolutely necessary.

After ten minutes or so of futile signalling to every vehicle that passed we finally gave a bigger than usual wave to a large frozen-food lorry, and it dutifully hissed to a halt. We all three got in, and Che Woofera got in too, and then we had to ask the driver to wait for a second while we got Che Woofera out again.

'Journey's end, Che,' we said in tough unemotional voices.

'Oh, I dunno,' said Che, as he landed deftly on his forepaws. 'I'd quite fancy a ride at this time of the evening.'

'Nothing doing,' we told him. 'So long, old son. It's been nice knowing you.'

'Have it your own way,' said Che philosophically. And he sat there propped up against a road-sign until we were out of sight.

We fell silent.

'You know,' I said, 'if it hadn't been for Offa and his half-dozey dyke-digging we could have had that dog's company for another day at least. Offa should have fenced the thing off. You can't have rabbit-warrens on an earthwork.'

Then we rounded on Offa, and we tore him to shreds. We called him an incompetent and a megalomaniac. We cast doubts upon his generalship, and we said his monetary policy was a disaster. We said he was the Mercians' answer to Inspector Clouseau, and they only put the crown on his head so they could get it down again if they needed it in a hurry. We said his parents were notorious wasters, and his courtiers were the laugh of the kingdom, and as for his surveyors and his military architects – ha!

The worst of this lot – the surveyors and the military architects, I mean – was a self-satisfied bodger of the name of Aelfroth the Unready. In Anglo-Saxon terms Aelfroth the Unready was about as highly-charged and dynamic as Gardeners' Question Time.

'Dig it deep and dig it well, me lads,' he would pronounce roundly as he rolled his expert eye over the latest ten-mile stretch that he had been charged with desecrating. 'The turf that's on top must go under the lot – as my old dad used to say.'

The five Welsh slaves that have been allocated to the work stare around them in frustration. 'But we've only got one spade between us, look you.'

'Ar,' says the sage. 'Oi was wondering when you was going to spot that. Well ... hmmm ... ho ... ar ... hm. There's nowt to be mended that can't be lended. Let me see now – David, lad.'

'Yes?' said a conscript harpist guardedly.

'Ar. Now, David, lad. Shall you nip over to that farm down there in the valley and ask the farmer – noicely-like, mind – if he'd oblige us with a couple of spades for six months. No –' the veteran surveyor tests the hardness of the ground with his heel – 'Say a year. Better say a year. If you over-estimate the toime, you're doin' foine, as we say.'

The harpist sets off.

'Now,' says Aelfroth. 'You, lad. What's your name?'

'Mifanwy.'

'Ar. Miffy, I calls you. Roight then, Miffy. Let you and me mark out the loin we'll be working to. Now take this 'ere coil of string and back yer go.'

'How far back?'

'As far as the loin will take you, me boy.'

'But the string's a good half mile long,' Mifanwy points out with a blend of hope and incredulity.

'A loin that's long is a loin that's strong,' Aelfroth reassures him. And the second slave in as many minutes disappears over the hilltop and goes back home to Wales.

The remaining three hang around for half an hour, and then one of them has a bright idea and asks if he can spend a penny. He is last seen making for a dense coppice which ought to give him the privacy he needs.

Aelfroth takes the loss of men imperturbably. 'One spade between two will see you through,' he explains to the surviving pair as he sorts them out some woolly blankets for the night.

Of course, Aelfroth's incompetence is pretty well known along the Dyke. On the other hand he does have his uses. If nothing else he knows how to handle the King. Those random and petulant visits to the Welsh marches are water off a duck's back as far as Aelfroth is concerned.

'Grand Artificer, what the devil's going on *here*?' demands the King querulously, suddenly riding up to the unstarted section that should have been finished months ago. 'You told me all this was supposed to be ready.'

The Grand Artificer looks blankly at the Warden of the March, who looks blankly at his lieutenant, who administers a salutary dressing-down to the draughtsman.

'The season's too wet, sire,' comes back up the line.

'Too wet? But good heavens we're in July! I can jolly well dig when it's wet. Can't you dig when it's wet, Grand Artificer?'

'Very much so, sire.'

'Do you want me to show you how to dig when it's wet?'

'Up to a point, sire.'

'Well then, if I can do it why can't they? That's the trouble with you, Grand Artificer. I get nothing but excuses the whole bally time. Who's in charge of this section anyway?'

The Grand Artificer looks blankly at the Warden of the March, who turns to his lieutenant, who scowls at the draughtsman, who looks the name up on the scroll. An expression of dawning comprehension passes across the faces of the officers as Aelfroth's name travels the reverse way along the row.

'One Aelfroth, sire. Known as The Unready.'

'Aelfroth the Unready, eh? You're telling *me* he's unready. The man doesn't even seem to be here.'

'Here oi be, yer gracious majesty. Here oi be,' rumbles the surveyor, emerging from behind a hedge where he has been dozing in amongst his floral clock. 'Aelfroth, yer humble servant, at your Majesty's service.'

'Ah! The Grand Artificer tells me its too wet to dig. What do you say to that, eh?'

'Too wet to dig?' says Aelfroth. 'Well, bless my ears, it's never too wet to dig. What His Eminence means, Yer Majesty, is that it isn't wet *enough* to dig *proper*, which is just another way of putting it. It's all down to what we calls yer toime and motion, see,' he continues. 'You can dig it all right. You can *dig* it and yer'll get a job – o' sorts. But now, you let that soaky old rain drain in for another week or more and yer'll lift it off like butter. Give it ten days and that'll come off, Yer Majesty, if yer'll pardon the expression, like a lad off a closet.'

'I see. Why wasn't this explained to me before? Grand Artificer, did you know this about the effects of rain on turf?'

'Oh yes, sire,' says the Grand Artificer, lying in his teeth.

'Well, it seems a very strange thing to me that you didn't mention it. So that means presumably that you've moved the men to another site.'

'Presumably,' says the Grand Artificer. He has been wondering where the men were ever since his arrival on Aelfroth's patch.

'Well, come along, Grand Artificer, come along. Let's get ourselves to where they are and see what it is they're doing.'

The King and his officers ride away as Aelfroth goes back to his floral clock for some light hoeing before tea.

That's how the Dyke was built.

The lorry driver asked us where we wanted to go, and we said within reason to wherever he happened to be going. He said he was going to Hereford first and then to Ross-on-Wye.

We discussed the merits of the two places, Henry arguing

against Hereford, of course, on the grounds that it is a Cathedral city.

After a while the lorry driver suggested we toss for it, and I could see his point of view. It can't be every day of the week you give a lift to three men and a dog who then proceed to abandon the dog and immediately begin wondering out loud where it is they think they are going. We asked him which he would recommend, and he said Ross-on-Wye was good for Bingo. This was an attraction which hadn't occurred to us before, and Henry and I, who had been rooting for Ross-on-Wye from the start, said that that decided the matter.

It put a new slant on tourism, this opinion from behind the steering-wheel. It helped us to see towns in a new light. It made us realise how much more could be achieved to attract the visitor to England and to Europe if only the proper amenities were laid on. Take Stratford-on-Avon, for example. A pleasant enough little spot in its way, but not a whisper of a roller-skating rink from one end of the town to the other. Then there's the British Museum, which has been short of a decent disco for years. And the continentals are no better. At Mont St. Michel – I have it on good authority – the lack of betting-shops is nothing more nor less than a public scandal. In Heidelberg you can't find a whelk-stall for love nor money, and as for the Uffizi Gallery in Florence the tour operators have given them fair warning: If they don't get themselves properly organised this year and make the space for a full-sized clock-golf in the courtyard they'll be struck off the list of Grade A Attractions and have to make do with art lovers and history students to bring in the money. Then where will they be?

The lorry driver's rather individualistic view of what makes a tourist spot set me thinking of my sister's second husband Hymie on a never-to-be-forgotten visit to *H.M.S. Victory* at Portsmouth. Individualism encased his whole trip like breadcrumbs round a schnitzel.

Hymie came from New York, and his courtship of Frances was such a whirlwind affair that the first thing the family knew about it was when we got a snapshot of the happy couple standing outside the register office. It was a cleverly taken picture and it made Hymie look normal. Then the following summer he sprang off a boat at Southampton to find out about his new relations.

'Whirlwind' not only goes to describe Hymie's romance – it gives a fairly good impression of his effect on Nelson's flagship as well.

He was small and festooned with cameras. 'Unbelievable belly-dancing lovelies swam out with them off the Azores,' he told me as I hurried him to a taxi.

At the *Victory* dry-dock he photographed a grey-bearded admiral who is kept on the quayside to impress visitors. 'They doan make 'em like that any more,' he explained to the film as he wound it on. Then he eyed the admiral directly for the first time.

'Ya got sumpin ta show me?' he demanded.

'Nelson's flagship, my good sir. The ship from which he won Trafalgar.'

'Okay. So he died winning. You gotta customer.'

On board he ran riot. 'What's da headroom in here?' he demanded of the Petty Officer who led our party into the gun deck.

'Five foot two inches, sir. They had to work in a confined space in those days.'

'Yah? So who's handling the fire risk? Strike a light in here and you grill yourself a sailor sandwich.'

'That's hardly the point ...'

'And another thing,' said Hymie. 'What's da headroom in the captain's solarium?'

'Please be quiet,' said an exasperated man on his left. 'You are ruining the tour for everybody else.'

Hymie turned on this unfortunate an unwavering, goldfish stare. 'You,' he intoned, 'are an uncouth youth. Crude, rude and tatooed.'

By this time fellow Americans in the party were beginning to cast around for a way out of their embarrassment. 'Just look at these brasses!' gasped one lady desperately. 'Why, you can see your face in them!'

'We know dat, sweetheart,' came back from the motionless Hymie. 'Try counting the benefits.'

The three minutes silence round the spot where Nelson fell were counted away by the clicking of Hymie's shutters. Then we all trooped down the gangplank again to shake hands with the admiral before we left.

'Interesting ship, don't you think?' he said as Hymie

approached.

'Uhu – you gotta good boat,' Hymie told him man to man. A crisp five dollar bill slapped down into the admiral's incredulous palm. 'Now fix yourself some noo whiskers.'

The lorry driver put us down at the Falcon Hotel at Ross-on-Wye and, cheerfully refusing our invitation to join us for a drink, he drove off into the dusk.

The Hotel Manager met us at the door. He said he wasn't authorised to do anything for us officially, but if we went round to the back the chef might be able to spare a few scraps.

I said No, we were looking for a room for the night, which seemed to take him aback, but he recovered strongly and told us that he was fully booked. The dining-room – which was completely empty – was fully booked as well.

I turned round to Fraser and Henry to remonstrate. But I never got the words out. I suppose it was catching sight of them full-face under the neon lights that made me waver. The effects of five days hit-and-miss shaving with his newfangled razor had left Fraser looking like an abandoned forestry scheme. He was carrying his back-pack in his arms, and hanging off it by two separate strings were a tin mug and a large piece of cheese which he had pierced in the middle in order to thread the cord through.

Henry was perspiring pretty freely – he often does – and he hardly helped our case by choosing this particular moment to mop his face with the lower portion of his shirt, thus revealing a generous expanse of torso to the young lady behind the Reservations desk. I raised my hand at the manager to justify our presence, and found that I was still carrying my boot.

Shoulder to shoulder we faced up to the man squarely. Then everything went black – at least it did for me.

'Boo!' said a voice, and there was my very own Widget playfully blindfolding her husband with an amusing little headscarf in tartan folkweave which she had bought for the knockdown sum of £17.50.

Yes, it was Widget and Katrina and Penny, who with the intelligence and instinct of women had made their way from Hereford to Ross that very day, and had even now been sitting in elegant seclusion in a corner of the lounge knocking back the

Cinzanos before dinner. What a riot of adventures they had had. Widget had bought her scarf, and Penny had seen a painting which looked as if it might have been a Giorgione ... But first the small matter of accommodation for the night.

I must say the Manager of the Falcon Hotel was a resourceful fellow. For a man who had no accommodation to spare, the way he was able to transform three single rooms for the girls into three doubles with bath – Henry insisted on the bath, and Fraser and I said we agreed he needed one – was little short of a miracle. It seems to me that, if you stare long enough into that big book which hotel managers keep, there is virtually no limit to the number of people you can find space for.

So we had our baths, and we came down and we called for sherry, and then we dined in splendid isolation in the cavernous dining-room. And the girls asked if we were going on the next day, and Henry and Fraser said that unfortunately my foot prevented them from doing so. And the girls said they would be perfectly happy to nurse me for the next couple of days; but Henry and Fraser said that it wouldn't be the same without me, and Fraser added that he'd just remembered he'd promised to meet a man in a pub the following night to discuss something important, so he had to get back.

I did some serious thinking over my cheese. Then I opened my eyes and started to say: 'What –' And everybody laughed at me rather loudly.

I said with dignity: 'I was about to say, what have you girls been up to for the past week?'

'And I am answering,' said Widget, 'that we'll tell you that at breakfast. It's time you went to bed.'

Of course they never told us at breakfast. First of all I forgot to ask, and on top of that there was an incident.

The manager approached – they never seem to get any sleep these fellows. He said: 'You wouldn't happen to be the owners of a small terrier with a black patch over one eye would you, gentlemen? It's hanging around the carpark and it doesn't seem to want to go away.'

Fraser said: 'We are not the owners of that dog. That dog is an independent operator. However, you will oblige me by asking the chef to give it a large bone with my compliments. Charge the bone to my account. Oh – and Mr Hoskins, please tell the dog that it is a contribution to party funds.'

But Penny said: 'I have never heard of anything so callous in my life. That dog is coming home with me. I'm sure he's an absolute pet.'

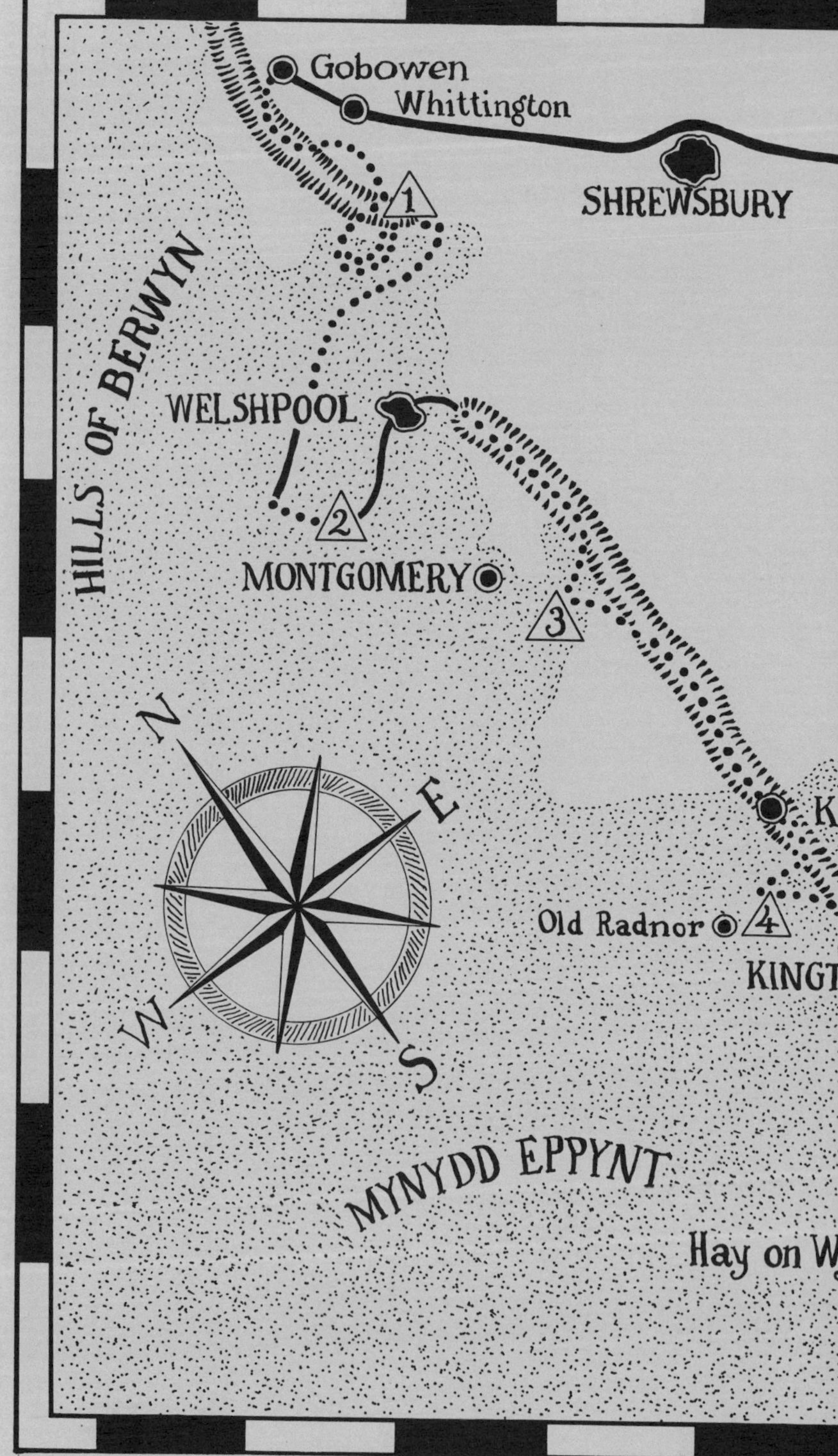

Gobowen
Whittington
SHREWSBURY
1
HILLS OF BERWYN
WELSHPOOL
2
MONTGOMERY
3
N
E
W
S
Old Radnor
4
MYNYDD EPPYNT